READING

- Comprehension • Spelling • Grammar • Review

4

Blake
e
LEARNING

Contents

Year Planner

	Week 1	Week 2	Week 3	Week 4	Week 5	Week 6	Week 7	Week 8	Week 9
Comprehension	Making predictions	Figurative language	Making connections	Main idea and details	Finding facts and information	Main idea and details	Compare and contrast	Sequencing events	Drawing conclusions
Spelling	Long vowels	Digraphs: ew, ue, ui	Trigraphs: air, eer, ear	Suffix: ing	Plurals: s, es	Soft c and g	Endings: le, el, al	Ending: ge	Suffix: ed
Grammar	Common and proper nouns	Capital letters and periods	Abstract nouns	Capital letters in titles	Personal and reflexive pronouns	Verbs	Auxiliary verbs	Progressive tense	Commas in lists
Review	Spelling			Grammar			Comprehension		

	Week 10	Week 11	Week 12	Week 13	Week 14	Week 15	Week 16	Week 17	Week 18
Comprehension	Point of view	Cause and effect	Sequencing events	Analyzing character actions	Word study	Main idea and details	Audience and purpose	Visualization	Important information
Spelling	Prefixes: un, dis, mis	Plurals: s, ies	Endings: ice, ise, ize	Suffixes: er, est	Digraphs: ie and ei	Suffix: ly	Homophones	Endings: ent, ant	Compound words
Grammar	Adjective order	Adverbs	Adjectives and adverbs	Determiners	Noun phrases	Prepositions	Prepositional phrases	Fronted adverbials	Possessive nouns
Review	Spelling			Grammar			Comprehension		

	Week 19	Week 20	Week 21	Week 22	Week 23	Week 24	Week 25	Week 26	Week 27
Comprehension	Figurative language	Analyzing character actions	Audience and purpose	Making inferences	Important information	Compare and contrast	Making inferences	Cause and effect	Word study
Spelling	Past tense	Endings: or, ure	Digraphs: wh, ph, gh	Vowel sound y	Digraph: ch	Endings: in, ine, ain	Suffix: ous	Prefixes: in, im, ir, il	Suffixes: ion, ation
Grammar	Punctuating dialogue	Frequently confused words	Reported speech	Punctuating quotations	Modal auxiliaries	Subjects and predicates	Correctly punctuate run-on sentences	Simple and compound sentences	Commas in compound sentences
Review	Spelling			Grammar			Comprehension		

	Week 28	Week 29	Week 30	Week 31	Week 32	Week 33	Week 34	Week 35	Week 36
Comprehension	Making connections	Making inferences	Word study	Compare and contrast	Finding facts and information	Making connections	Fact or opinion?	Compare and contrast	Drawing conclusions
Spelling	Prefixes: re, de, pre	Suffixes: ment, ship, hood, dom	Endings: ery, ary, ory	Suffixes: able, ible	Latin origins	Tricky words	Suffix: ly	Letter patterns: cc, xc	Greek origins
Grammar	Subordinate clauses	Relative pronouns	Relative adverbs	Relative clauses	Questions and exclamations	Exclamation points for effect	Compound and complex sentences	Spoken and written English	Punctuate a variety of sentences
Review	Spelling			Grammar			Comprehension		

The Goats

Making predictions

We can predict what is going to happen in a text based on clues in the words and pictures, and what we already know.

Read the passage.

Circle what the goats did to the children.

Underline why Mr. Kent was pleased with the goats.

Put a box around where Mr. Kent was when he saw the crabs.

Highlight how Mr. Kent was standing when he looked at the crabs.

Color why Mr. Kent was excited.

Lots of children heard about the goats and came to visit. Morecambe and Wise put their heads down and butted them in all directions. The children thought it was great fun—that is, the ones that got away did. The children who didn't escape went home crying and told their mothers.

Mr. Kent smiled when he saw what was happening. "These goats are as good as a watchdog," he said. "This'll put a stop to whoever is stealing our strawberries."

Mr. Kent wasn't so happy the next day.

He was at the dam. He leaned forward, then called excitedly to Mrs. Kent, "We've got some baby crabs! Hurray!"

Circle your answers for each question.

1 What three predictions can you make about what will happen next in the story?

a One of the goats will butt Mr. Kent.   b Mr. Kent will push the goats into the dam.

c Mr. Kent will be angry.   d Mrs. Kent will push Mr. Kent into the dam.

e Mr. Kent will get wet.   f The goats will eat the baby crabs.

2 What **evidence** is there in the text to support your predictions? Select two answers.

a Mr. Kent was excited about the crabs.

b Some of the children got away from the goats.

c The goats have shown that they like to butt people.

d Someone had been stealing the Kents' strawberries.

e The children didn't like it when the goats butted them.

f Mr. Kent was in the right position to get butted.

RL.4.1 Refer to details and examples in a text when explaining what the text says explicitly and when drawing inferences from the text.

The Goats

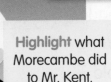

Read the whole story

The Goats

by Elizabeth Best
Illustrated by Janine Dawson

Read the passage.

Circle how Mrs. Kent felt when she saw that the children were missing.

Put a box around what Wise did to Mrs. Kent.

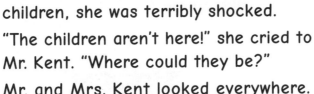

When Mrs. Kent went in to wake the children, she was terribly shocked.

"The children aren't here!" she cried to Mr. Kent. "Where could they be?"

Mr. and Mrs. Kent looked everywhere. They looked inside the house and outside the house.

Morecambe starting butting his head against Mr. Kent as he searched near the shed.

Wise started pushing against Mrs. Kent while she peered under the car.

"The goats are trying to tell us something," said Mr. Kent.

"Let's untie them and see what they do," replied Mrs. Kent.

Highlight what Morecambe did to Mr. Kent.

Underline what Mr. Kent said to Mrs. Kent.

1 What do you **think** the goats are going to do after Mr. and Mrs. Kent untie them?

_____

_____

_____

2 What **evidence** is there in the text that helped you make your **prediction**?

_____

_____

_____

_____

_____

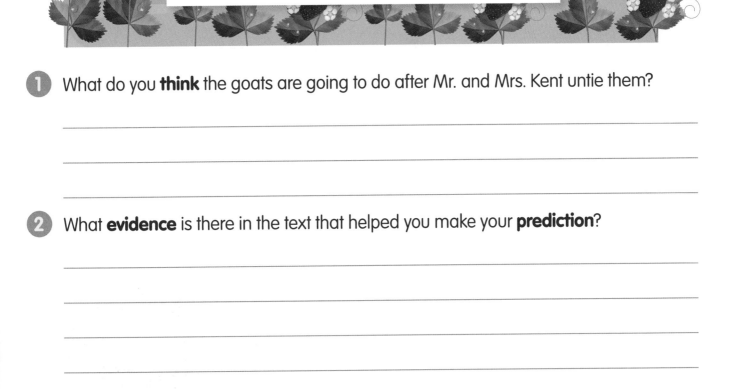

RL.4.1 Refer to details and examples in a text when explaining what the text says explicitly and when drawing inferences from the text.

3

Long vowels

Long vowels are pronounced like their alphabet sound. The vowel **o** is usually **long** when it comes at the **end of a word**; e.g., pian**o**.

The vowels **i** and **o** have a long sound when followed by **two or more consonants**; e.g., ch**i**ld, b**o**th.

When **e** is added to a word containing **a short vowel**, the short vowel becomes a **long vowel**. This is called a split digraph; e.g., fin → fin**e**.

List ❶ Write the word.

spade _____
throne _____
bold _____
most _____
spine _____
flute _____
only _____
strike _____
ninth _____
wild _____
estate _____
explode _____
taste _____
awhile _____
broken _____
radio _____
alone _____
evening _____
surprise _____
divide _____

❷ Name.

a _____   b _____

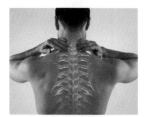

c _____   d _____

❸ Fill in the missing letters.

a b __ l __   b __ w __ i __ e
c o __ __ y   d b __ o __ __ n
e s __ r __ __ e   f __ a __ i __
g e __ ta __ __   h a __ o __ __
i ex __ __ o __ __   j __ ur __ __ i __ __

❹ Word clues. Which list word means?

a you can listen to music on it _____
b this comes before tenth _____
c not tame _____
d you dig holes with this _____
e not with other people _____
f something unexpected _____

4   L.4.2.D Spell grade-appropriate words correctly.

Long vowels

1 **Revise your spelling list from page 4.** Underline the spelling mistakes.
Write the word correctly.

a We used a spayd to dig holes for our new plants. _____

b She liked chocolate the moste. _____

c We are planning a suprise birthday party for my brother. _____

d The lemon had a bitter, sour tayst. _____

e It was May the nineth. _____

f The floot is my favorite musical instrument. _____

g We had to devide the last piece of cake equally. _____

h The wyld dog barked loudly. _____

Challenge words

2 **Write the word.**

ozone _____

unite _____

imitate _____

devoted _____

idle _____

suppose _____

satellite _____

phrase _____

produce _____

barricade _____

3 **Word clues.** Which challenge word means?

a very loving and loyal _____

b to copy someone's actions _____

c something in space _____

d used to block the way _____

e a gas _____

f to join together _____

g not active or in use _____

h a group of words _____

i to make something _____

j to consider possible _____

4 **Complete the sentence with a challenge word.**

a She always manages to _____ the best short stories.

b I struggled to _____ my words correctly.

c The scientists sent their latest _____ into space.

d I _____ you can come to the beach with us.

e The _____ layer absorbs most of the Sun's energy.

Common and proper nouns

A **noun** names something. Nouns that refer to **general** people, places, and things are called **common nouns**; e.g., boy, bird, river, chair. Nouns that refer to **specific** people, places, things, days, and months are called **proper nouns**; e.g., Joe, Amazon, April.

1 **Complete each sentence with a noun from the box.**

| Grand Canyon | knife | mountain | cheese | Mount Everest |

a I cut the fruit with a sharp _____ .

b I added a slice of _____ to my sandwich.

c When I went to Arizona, I saw the _____ .

d The highest _____ in the world is _____ .

2 **Name.** Golden Gate Bridge   zebra   The White House

a _____   b _____   c _____

3 **Sort the nouns.**

| elephant | Joseph | computer | Brazil | table |
| Saturday | pelican | April | Charlie | branch |

a **Common nouns**

_____
_____
_____
_____
_____

b **Proper nouns**

_____
_____
_____
_____
_____

6

Getting Rid of Wrinkles

Read the passage.

Underline the simile in paragraph 1.

Circle the animal that Great Grandpop compares Great Grandma to.

Tessa's Great Grandma Em had a face like a sheet of scrunched up newspaper. Great Grandpop Alfred teased her lots.

"You look like a hippopotamus that has been bathing in the river too long," he said at breakfast.

"The bags under your eyes could carry the treasure from a sunken pirate ship," he said at lunch.

Color the simile in paragraph 2.

Highlight the metaphor in paragraph 3.

Circle the correct answer for each question.

1 What is Great Grandma Em's face **compared** to?
- a   a sheet
- b   a hippopotamus
- c   a newspaper
- d   a sheet of scrunched up newspaper

2 The figure of speech in paragraph 1 is a **simile**. Which word tells us this?
- a   a
- b   like
- c   of
- d   sheet

3 What does the **simile** in paragraph 1 **suggest** about Great Grandma Em's face? Her face is ...
- a   very thin.
- b   quite hard.
- c   full of wrinkles.
- d   very smooth.

4 What does Great Grandpop Alfred **compare** the bags under Great Grandma's eyes to? Bags that can carry ...
- a   pirate treasure.
- b   pirates.
- c   ships.
- d   sunken ships.

5 The figure of speech in paragraph 3 is a **metaphor**. What does it **suggest** about the bags under Great Grandma's eyes? The bags under her eyes are ...
- a   colorful.
- b   valuable.
- c   big.
- d   sparkly.

Getting Rid of Wrinkles

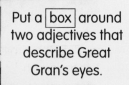

Read the whole story

Read the passage.

Underline three similes in paragraph 1.

Circle the words in paragraph 1 that show that the figures of speech are similes.

By the time the big day arrived, Great Gran's skin was as smooth as whipped cream, her cheeks were as rosy as ripe strawberries, and her eyes were like rich, dark chocolate drops.

"You're as lovely as the day I first saw you running across the field from the Maloney's prize bull," said Great Grandpop as he waltzed her around the living room.

Put a box around two adjectives that describe Great Gran's eyes.

Highlight the adjective that suggests that Great Gran had no wrinkles.

1. Great Gran's skin is compared to whipped cream. What picture of her skin does this create?

_____

_____

2. Great Gran's cheeks are described as being rosy. They are compared to ripe strawberries. Do you think this is a good comparison? Why, or why not?

_____

_____

_____

3. What picture do we get of Great Gran's eyes from the comparison: *Her eyes were like rich, dark chocolate drops?*

_____

_____

4. Choose one of the **similes** in paragraph 1 and write it as a **metaphor**.

_____

_____

L.4.5 Demonstrate understanding of figurative language, word relationships, and nuances in word meanings.

Digraphs: ew, ue, ui

Two letters that make a single sound are called a **digraph**. The letters **ew** make the long sound **u**; e.g., cr**ew**. The letters **ue** make the long sounds **oo** or **u**; e.g., f**ue**l or arg**ue**. The letters **ui** make the sound **oo**; e.g., fr**ui**t.

List ① Write the word.

dew _____

blew _____

true _____

skew _____

clue _____

suit _____

stew _____

chew _____

fruit _____

threw _____

jewel _____

rescue _____

nephew _____

venue _____

argue _____

continue _____

juice _____

value _____

cashew _____

avenue _____

② Name.

a _____   b _____

c _____   d _____

③ Chunks. Rearrange the chunks to make a list word.

a ew sh ca _____

b ce j ui _____

c in con ue t _____

d ue av en _____

e ph ne ew _____

④ In a group. Write the list word that belongs in each group.

a niece, cousin, _____

b chomp, bite, _____

c almond, peanut, _____

d price, worth, _____

e street, road, _____

f diamond, gem, _____

g save, free, _____

h hint, evidence, _____

i grape, apple, _____

j flung, tossed, _____

k debate, disagree, _____

l soup, broth, _____

Digraphs: ew, ue, ui

1 **Revise your spelling list from page 9.** Sort the words.

ew	ue	ui

Challenge words

2 **Write the word.**

issue _____

mildew _____

sluice _____

retinue _____

askew _____

pursue _____

residue _____

pewter _____

sinew _____

jewelry _____

3 **Word clues.** Which challenge word means?

a a channel where water flows _____

b a type of metal _____

c a fungus _____

d something that's left over _____

e tendon or ligament _____

f not straight or level _____

g body ornaments _____

h to follow or chase _____

4 **Complete the sentence.**

a My mother has a lot of gold _____.

b After walking home in the rain, Grandma's hat sat _____.

c The tape left a sticky _____ on my skin.

Capital letters and periods

Sentences start with a **capital letter** and end with a period (.), question mark (?), or exclamation point (!). Other words in a sentence that need a capital letter are:

- the personal pronoun **I**
- the names of specific people, places, things, days, and months (proper nouns); e.g., **Sam**, **Rodeo Drive**, **Mount Rushmore**, **Monday**, **April**.

1 **In the following sentences, underline the words that need a capital letter.**

a   we are going to watch oliver play soccer.

b   myra and i are catching the bus to the beach today.

c   we stayed in a small town called beaufort.

d   he is coming to fix the leak on wednesday.

e   the capital city of mississippi is jackson.

f   our dog bailey likes to dig holes in the garden.

g   my birthday is at the beginning of october.

2 **Rewrite the following paragraph with the periods and capital letters in the right places.**

yesterday i went to the zoo with my friends, simon and lauren we had a great time looking at all the animals our favorites were the chimpanzees and gorillas we also liked the bird show

_____

_____

_____

_____

3 **Complete the following sentences.** Don't forget the capital letters and periods.

a   My favorite place to visit is _____

b   I am reading a book about a dog called _____

Tokyo Techno

Read the passage.

Making connections
Linking a text to other texts you have read is a great way to build understanding. Look for key words and phrases in the texts to make the connections.

Anita unfolded a map of Japan.

"It says the capital of Japan is Tokyo. That's where we're going." She read on, "Japan is made up of four main islands and over 3,000 little ones." Anita marked Tokyo, on the island of Honshu, with a red spot.

In the corner of the map Jason pointed to a white flag with a red circle in the middle. "That's the Japanese flag," he said. "The word Japan actually means *source of the sun*."

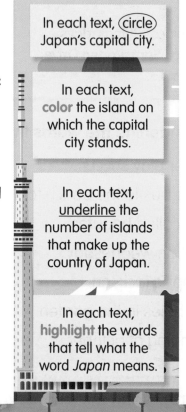

In each text, circle Japan's capital city.

In each text, **color** the island on which the capital city stands.

In each text, underline the number of islands that make up the country of Japan.

In each text, **highlight** the words that tell what the word *Japan* means.

Japan is a country in the Pacific Ocean. It consists of four main islands and thousands of smaller ones. The capital city, Tokyo, is on the island of Honshu.

Japan is known as the *Land of the Rising Sun*. This is because its name means *sun origin*.

Japan is on the Pacific Ring of Fire. It experiences over 1,500 earthquakes every year. In 2011, a huge earthquake and tsunami caused a lot of damage.

Circle the correct answers.

1 Which information appears in both texts?

  a Japan consists of many islands.

  b The capital city of Japan is Tokyo.

  c Japan is on the Pacific Ring of Fire.

  d Tokyo is on the island of Honshu.

  e Japan often experiences earthquakes.

  f Four of Japan's islands are bigger than the others.

  g Japan is known as the *Land of the Rising Sun*.

  h The word Japan means *where the sun comes from*.

RL.4.1 Refer to details and examples in a text when explaining what the text says explicitly and when drawing inferences from the text.

Tokyo Techno

Read the whole story

Read the passage.

Jason looked out the train window. Beyond the rice fields he could see a huge snow-capped mountain. "That mountain looks like an old volcano."

"It is. Japan is full of volcanoes," said Toshi. "That's Mt. Fuji, Japan's most famous mountain."

Jason pulled an instant camera out of his bag and took a photo. On the bottom he wrote 'Mount Fuji, JAPAN—famous old volcano.'

Underline the words in each text that give the same information about Mount Fuji.

Color the words in each text that give different information about Mount Fuji.

In each text, highlight the phrases that tell what passengers on the train often do when they pass Mount Fuji.

Mount Fuji is Japan's highest and most famous mountain. It has been worshipped as a sacred mountain for centuries.

Mount Fuji is an active volcano. It last erupted in 1708.

A good way to view Mount Fuji is from the train on the trip between Tokyo and Osaka. Tourists can often be seen taking photographs of Mount Fuji from the train windows.

1. What do **both** texts tell us about Mount Fuji?

_____

_____

_____

2. What **extra information** about Mount Fuji do we get if we look at the texts separately?

_____

_____

_____

3. Imagine you are planning a trip to Japan. How would these two texts help you decide on the best way to view Mount Fuji?

_____

_____

_____

RL.4.1 Refer to details and examples in a text when explaining what the text says explicitly and when drawing inferences from the text.

Trigraphs: air, eer, ear

Three letters that make a single sound are called a **trigraph**. The letters **air** make the single sound **air**; e.g., h**air**. The letters **eer** make the single sound **ear**; e.g., d**eer**. The letters **ear** make the single sounds **ear**, **air**, or **er**; e.g., h**ear**, p**ear**, **ear**th.

List ① Write the word.

steer _____

near _____

lair _____

smear _____

early _____

beard _____

Earth _____

pearl _____

search _____

clear _____

eerie _____

weary _____

yearn _____

fairly _____

earnings _____

research _____

dreary _____

despair _____

pioneer _____

prairie _____

② Name.

a _____   b _____

③ Word clues. Which list word means?

a to long for _____

b home of a wild animal _____

c stubble on a man's face _____

d found in an oyster _____

e one of the first to do something _____

f our planet _____

g tired _____

h gloomy or sad _____

i grassland _____

j mysterious _____

④ In a group. Write the list word that belongs in each group.

a look, hunt, _____

b wage, pay, _____

c study, investigation, _____

d Saturn, Mars, _____

e plain, grassland, _____

f spooky, creepy, _____

Trigraphs: air, eer, ear

1 **Revise your spelling list from page 14.** Sort the words.

air	eer	ear	

Challenge words

2 **Write the word.**

rehearse _____

earnest _____

puppeteer _____

veneer _____

millionaire _____

engineer _____

buccaneer _____

volunteer _____

auctioneer _____

questionnaire _____

3 **Hidden words.** Find the challenge word.

a llimmillionairemiloae _____

b cabuccaneerbucne _____

c ionququestionnaireti _____

d hesrerehearsehsere _____

e arnerearnestarn _____

f uttpepuppeteerpuet _____

g sprquengineereertie _____

h rbqusveneerhhwic _____

i jkrsliauctioneererien _____

j eartervolunteerlunve _____

4 **Complete the sentence.**

a The _____ moved his characters effortlessly.

b The actors are meeting to _____ their upcoming play.

c The _____ is working on a design for a new bridge.

d My sister is a _____ at the local pound.

e The _____ was worried when nobody wanted to make a bid.

Abstract nouns

A **noun** names something. Nouns that name **thoughts**, **qualities**, and **feelings** are called **abstract nouns**; e.g., fear, love, patience.

1 Complete each sentence with an abstract noun.

Someone who can <u>imagine</u> faraway places has a good <u>imagination</u>.

a Places where people <u>laugh</u> a lot are filled with _____.

b If you can <u>remember</u> things, you have a good _____.

c People who are always <u>lucky</u> have _____ on their side.

d People who have <u>comfortable</u> surroundings live in _____.

e The boy who is <u>fascinated</u> by spiders has a _____ for spiders.

f Geologists who are <u>curious</u> about volcanoes have a _____ about volcanoes.

···

2 State whether the underlined nouns are common, proper, or abstract nouns.

a They live in the little <u>house</u> on the hill. _____

b Her work has shown a great <u>improvement</u>. _____

c I like looking at the shapes the <u>clouds</u> make. _____

d I bought the souvenirs when I went to <u>Italy</u> last year. _____

e The two little boys are always getting into <u>mischief</u>. _____

f I live on the corner of Castle Street and <u>Banks Lane</u>. _____

···

3 Write a sentence with each abstract noun.

a joy _____

_____

b freedom _____

_____

c kindness _____

_____

L.4.1 Demonstrate command of the conventions of standard English grammar and usage when writing or speaking.

Tiddalik the Frog

Read the passage.

Circle the word that tells how Tiddalik was feeling.

Highlight the noun that tells what Tiddalik needed.

Narrator: Long ago in the Dreaming, when the world was formed, Tiddalik the frog woke very thirsty one morning.

Tiddalik: I need water, I need water, I need water ...

Narrator: So Tiddalik drank all the water he could find.

Tiddalik: [gulp] [gulp] [gulp] [gulp]

Narrator: He drank so much that every billabong and creek and every river and stream was emptied.

Put a box around the action verb that tells what Tiddalik did.

Underline the sentence that contains the main idea.

Circle the correct answer for each question.

1 What is the **main idea** or **key point** of the text?
  a   Tiddalik the frog was very thirsty.
  b   Tiddalik the frog gulped down the water.
  c   Tiddalik the frog lived long ago.
  d   Tiddalik the frog drank all the water.

2 Which word best **supports** the **main idea**?
  a   water   b   emptied   c   drank   d   thirsty

3 Which phrase best **supports** the **main idea**?
  a   every billabong and creek and every stream and river
  b   need water
  c   Long ago in the Dreamtime
  d   woke very thirsty

Tiddalik the Frog

Read the passage.

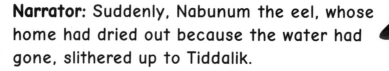

Underline the name of the animal that tried to make Tiddalik laugh.

Highlight the reason Tiddalik started giggling.

Color what Kookaburra thought was going to happen.

Put a box around the reason Wombat told everyone to stand back.

Narrator: Suddenly, Nabunum the eel, whose home had dried out because the water had gone, slithered up to Tiddalik.

Nabunum: Time for you to laugh, froggy.

Narrator: Nabunum began to dance, slowly at first, then faster and faster, wriggling into all sorts of shapes, knots, and twists. It worked! Tiddalik started giggling.

Kookaburra: I think he's going to burst.

Wombat: Stand back, here comes the water!

1 What is the **main idea** or **key point** of the text?

_____

_____

_____

2 List three **details** that **support** the **main idea**.

a _____

_____

_____

b _____

_____

_____

c _____

_____

_____

Suffix: ing

The suffix **ing** is added to a verb to show something is still happening. When the base form of the verb ends in a consonant with a <u>short vowel before</u> it, **double the consonant** before adding **ing**; e.g., dri<u>p</u> → dri**pp**ing, cla<u>p</u> → cla**pp**ing.

List **①** **Write the word.**

running _____

planning _____

digging _____

swimming _____

hopping _____

stunning _____

chatting _____

trapping _____

dripping _____

grinning _____

scrubbing _____

shrugging _____

throbbing _____

humming _____

wrapping _____

whizzing _____

chopping _____

propping _____

thudding _____

whipping _____

② **Word building.** Rewrite the word with the suffix **ing**.

a shrug _____

b throb _____

c whiz _____

d hum _____

e thud _____

f prop _____

g stun _____

h chat _____

③ **Missing vowels.** Fill in the missing vowels.

a pl ___ nn ___ ng   b scr ___ bb ___ ng

c tr ___ pp ___ ng   d d ___ gg ___ ng

e h ___ pp ___ ng   f shr ___ gg ___ ng

g wh ___ pp ___ ng   h h ___ mm ___ ng

i gr ___ nn ___ ng   j ch ___ pp ___ ng

k sw ___ mm ___ ng   l wh ___ zz ___ ng

m wr ___ pp ___ ng   n st ___ nn ___ ng

o th ___ dd ___ ng   p r ___ nn ___ ng

④ **Name.**

a _____ b _____ c _____ d _____

Suffix: ing

1 **Revise your spelling list from page 19.** Complete each sentence with a list word.

a   Dad was _____ wood for the fire.

b   The faucet was _____ and the noise kept me awake.

c   I could hear my mother _____ loudly on the phone.

d   My dog was _____ in the garden.

e   I couldn't wait for summer so I could go _____ in the pool.

f   They were _____ too fast for me to catch them.

g   We are _____ our next vacation.

Challenge words

2 **Write the word.**

forgetting   _____

forbidding   _____

committing   _____

regretting   _____

submitting   _____

worshipping   _____

formatting   _____

permitting   _____

transmitting   _____

equipping   _____

3 **Hidden words.** Find the challenge word.

a   oreforbiddingfoer   _____

b   tticocommittingted   _____

c   mitpermittingperti   _____

d   mittitransmittingts   _____

e   gdworshippingdf   _____

f   dfgvsubmittingfgd   _____

g   fequippingdfgrf   _____

h   vgdformattingvxd   _____

i   stregrettingetogvr   _____

TRESPASSING-
LOITERING
FORBIDDEN BY LAW

4 **Complete the sentence.**

a   She keeps _____ the words to the song.

b   I am _____ wearing my uncomfortable new shoes.

c   I was _____ the birthday card for Grandpa when my computer died.

d   He is _____ his art work for the competition tomorrow.

e   As we walked past the church, we could see people _____ inside.

f   Dad is _____ the car for our off road trip.

L.4.2.D Spell grade-appropriate words correctly.

Capital letters in titles

Most of the words in the title of a book, magazine, newspaper, poem, movie, or show start with a **capital letter**. Exceptions are articles (a, an, the) and prepositions, but not if they come at the beginning of the title; e.g., **C**harlie and the **C**hocolate **F**actory, **T**he **W**onderful **W**izard of **O**z.

1 **Check (✔) the titles that have the correct punctuation.**

a A Wrinkle in Time ☐   b Because Of Winn Dixie ☐

c Diary of a wimpy kid ☐   d Night at the Museum ☐

e Cat in the Hat ☐   f Despicable Me 2 ☐

g The Lost Hero ☐   h the Lion, the Witch and the Wardrobe ☐

i The Prince Of Egypt ☐   j Wind on the Hill ☐

2 **In each title, circle the letters that need a capital letter.**

a alice's adventures in wonderland   b the black stallion

c zlateh the goat   d dust of snow

e where the mountain meets the moon   f the making of a hurricane

g seeing eye to eye   h underground railroad

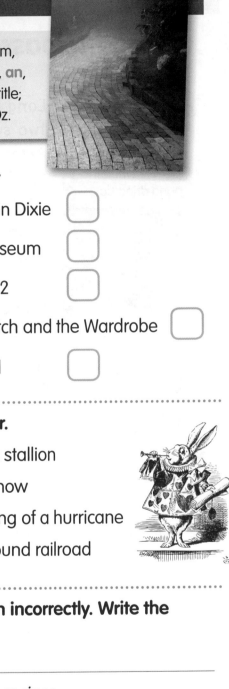

3 **In each title, underline the word that has been written incorrectly. Write the correction in the space.**

a My sister's favorite book is *Little women.* _____

b Roald Dahl wrote a book called *Completely Revolting recipes.*

_____

c A really funny poem is *Mother Doesn't Want A Dog,* by Judith Viorst.

_____

d *Toad Of Toad Hall* is a play by A. A. Milne. _____

e My aunt gave me *National geographic Kids* for my birthday.

_____

The Turtle Who Couldn't Stop Talking

Finding facts and information

To find facts and information in a text, ask the questions **Who? What? Where?** or **When?** The answers can be clearly seen in the text.

Read the passage.

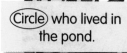

Circle who lived in the pond.

Underline when the pond dried up.

Long ago, a turtle lived in a pond with two swans. The turtle loved to talk. After a long drought, the pond dried up. The two swans realized they would have to find another pond.

"Don't leave me!" begged the turtle.

"But you can't fly," said the swans. "How can you come with us?" The turtle pleaded and pleaded. The swans at last came up with an idea.

Put a box around when the events in the story happened.

Highlight the turtle's words.

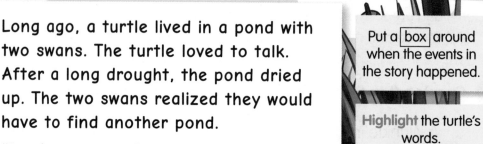

Circle the correct answer for each question.

1 **How many** creatures lived in the pond?

   a one   b three   c two   d four

2 **When** did the pond dry up?

   a long after the drought   b during the drought
   c after the long drought   d in the middle of the drought

3 **Who** decided to find another pond?

   a the turtle   b one of the swans   c the fish   d both swans

4 **What** did the turtle say?

   a "I can't fly!"   b "Come with me!"
   c "Don't leave me!"   d "Please help me!"

5 **When** did the events in the story happen?

   a not so long ago   b a long time ago
   c during the drought   d one hundred years ago

The Turtle Who Couldn't Stop Talking

Read the passage.

Underline what the turtle wanted to say when they flew high.

Highlight what the townspeople shouted.

Put a ⬚box around the reason the turtle opened his mouth.

Color what happened when the turtle let go of the stick.

When they flew high, the turtle wanted to say "Look at the beautiful view!" but he remembered the swans' warning. They passed over a small town. People looked up and shouted, "Look at that silly turtle!" The turtle wanted to cry out, "Mind your own business," but he again remembered the warning. As they flew on, more villagers spotted them. People began pointing and crying out, "Crazy swans! Crazy turtle!"

The turtle couldn't stand it any longer. He yelled out, "Go away foolish people!" But he let go of the stick and fell to the ground, landing on his back and cracking his shell into a thousand pieces.

1 **What** did the turtle want to say when he looked down at the view?

_____

_____

2 **Where** were they flying when the people shouted, "Look at that silly turtle!"?

_____

3 **When** did the turtle open his mouth?

_____

_____

4 **What** happened when the turtle opened his mouth?

_____

_____

RL.4.1 Refer to details and examples in a text when explaining what the text says explicitly and when drawing inferences from the text.

23

Plurals: s, es

You make most **plurals** by adding **s** to singular nouns. For nouns that end in **s**, **sh**, **ch**, **x**, and **z**, make them plural by adding **es**; e.g., 3 atla**ses**, 2 sket**ches**, 5 bo**xes**, 3 qui**zzes**.

For some nouns that end in **o**, add **es**; e.g., 4 potato**es**. Other nouns that end in **o** can take either **s** or **es**; e.g., mango**s** or mango**es**.

List

1 **Write the word.**

places _____

nurses _____

glasses _____

speeches _____

trumpets _____

ladders _____

leashes _____

winners _____

leaders _____

losses _____

minutes _____

visitors _____

authors _____

balloons _____

kangaroos _____

branches _____

radishes _____

quizzes _____

answers _____

radios _____

2 **Word building.** Rewrite each list word adding the suffix *s* or *es*.

a answer _____

b radish _____

c loss _____

d ladder _____

e kangaroo _____

f leash _____

g speech _____

h balloon _____

3 **In a group.** Write the list word that belongs in each group.

a guests, company, _____

b koalas, wallabies, _____

c talks, debates, _____

d seconds, hours, _____

e editors, publishers, _____

f horns, bugles, _____

4 **Word clues.** Which list word means?

a they look after you in hospital _____

b you climb them to reach high places _____

c brass instruments _____

d used to walk dogs _____

e animals that jump _____

f those who come first in an event _____

L.4.2.D Spell grade-appropriate words correctly.

Plurals: s, es

1 **Revise your spelling list from page 24.** Name.

a _____   b _____   c _____   d _____

Challenge words

2 **Write the word.**

spectators _____

referees _____

volcanoes _____

sandwiches _____

sombreros _____

blemishes _____

topazes _____

witnesses _____

passengers _____

gelatos _____

3 **Word clues.** Which challenge word matches?

a lava _____

b savoury food _____

c hats _____

d gems _____

e desserts _____

f travelers _____

g stains _____

h umpires _____

i audience _____

j observers _____

4 **Another way to say it.** Which challenge word could replace the underlined words?

a After dinner we all had <u>ice creams</u> for dessert. _____

b The <u>travelers</u> grew excited as the plane landed. _____

c When he was sick, his face was covered in <u>spots</u>. _____

d The football club decided to hire some new <u>umpires</u>. _____

e The <u>observers</u> cheered for the tennis champion. _____

f They were asked to give evidence as they were <u>bystanders</u>. _____

Personal and reflexive pronouns

Use pronouns in place of nouns to save repeating the nouns all
the time. We use **personal pronouns** in **place of people or things**;
e.g., **Lydia** is helping **Tom**. **She** is helping **him**.
We use reflexive pronouns to **refer back to a noun or pronoun**;
e.g., **Lydia** is helping herself to more ice cream.

1 **Color the pronouns to get to the finish line.**

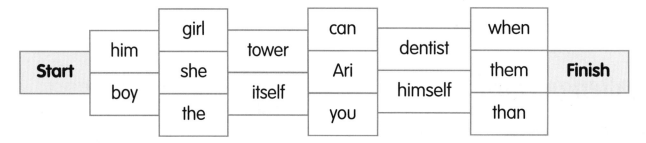

		girl		can		when	
Start	him		tower		dentist		Finish
	she			Ari		them	
	boy		itself		himself		
		the		you		than	

....

2 **Correct the word that is wrong.**

a   He helped heself to another chocolate.   _____

b   Mickey and me are going to the movies.   _____

c   They locked theyself in the bathroom.   _____

d   They said we had to do the work ourself.   _____

e   Me took the dog to the vet today.   _____

f   He and her are brother and sister.   _____

g   Him and I are in the same soccer team.   _____

....

3 **Complete each sentence with a pronoun.**

a   My cat cleans _____ using its tongue.

b   Her friend gave _____ some of her lunch.

c   My parents bought _____ a bicycle for my birthday.

d   The hikers made sure they took enough food with _____.

e   I always wave to Felix when _____ walks past my house.

L.4.1 Demonstrate command of the conventions of standard English grammar and usage when writing or speaking.

Homes

Finding the main idea and supporting details
To discover what a text is about, look for the main idea or key point. Facts and details in the text can help you find the main idea.

Read the passage.

Circle when most homes received electricity.

Underline the sentence that sums up the main idea of the passage.

Highlight what electric light bulbs replaced.

Most homes received electricity during the early 1900s. Rural homes had to wait longer. Many homes in developing countries still do not have electricity.

Electricity changed the way homes worked. Electric ovens and heaters replaced gas and wood-burning stoves. Electric light bulbs replaced kerosene lamps and gas lights. Electric refrigerators replaced iceboxes. Electricity also led to the invention of the telephone.

Color what electric ovens and heaters replaced.

Put a box around what refrigerators replaced.

Circle the invention that allows us to communicate with people who are far away.

Circle the correct answer/s for each question.

1 What is the passage **mainly** about?

a the reasons some homes do not have electricity

b the reason the telephone was invented

c when most homes received electricity

d how electricity has changed the way homes work

2 Which three **details support the main idea**?

a Electric ovens and heaters replaced gas and wood-burning stoves.

b City homes received electricity before rural homes.

c Many homes in developing countries still do not have electricity.

d Electric refrigerators replaced iceboxes.

e Most homes received electricity over a hundred years ago.

f Electric light bulbs replaced kerosene lamps and gas lights.

Homes

Read the passage.

Read the full text

Homes

Underline the sentence that sums up the main idea of the passage.

Highlight how bathrooms have changed through the years.

The layout of rooms in a home has changed as society has changed.

As plumbing improved, bathrooms became rooms inside the home, rather than outside.

Kitchens only became the center of homes in the last 60 years. Filled with new appliances, they are no longer hidden rooms used for hard, dirty work. They are linked to open-plan living and dining areas.

Informal living areas at the rear of homes replaced formal living rooms at the front. Living areas were linked to terraces and gardens to create outdoor rooms.

Color how kitchens have changed in the last 60 years.

Put a box around where informal living areas are found in modern homes.

1 Which sentence sums up what the passage is about?

_____

_____

_____

2 List three **details** that **support** the **main idea**.

a _____

_____

_____

b _____

_____

_____

c _____

_____

_____

RI.4.1 Refer to details and examples in a text when explaining what the text says explicitly and when drawing inferences from the text.

Soft c and g

In some words that contain **c**, the **c** sounds like the letter **k**. This is a hard **c** sound; e.g. **c**arrot. In other words that contain **c**, the **c** sounds like the letter **s**. This is a soft **c** sound; e.g., pea**c**e.

In some words that contain **g**, the **g** has its own sound of **g**. This is a hard **g** sound; e.g., **g**rapes. In other words that contain **g**, the **g** sounds like the letter **j**. This is a soft **g** sound; e.g., oran**g**es.

List ① **Write the word.**

price _____

germ _____

digit _____

agent _____

dance _____

parcel _____

large _____

legend _____

decide _____

danger _____

except _____

cyclone _____

accept _____

success _____

prince _____

choice _____

princess _____

saucer _____

energy _____

century _____

② **Sort the words.**

a Soft c

_____   _____

_____   _____

_____   _____

_____   _____

_____   _____

_____   _____

b Soft g

_____   _____

_____   _____

_____   _____

_____   _____

③ **Opposites.** Find the opposite.

a failure _____

b safety _____

c refuse _____

④ **Name.**

a _____   b _____   c _____   d _____

Soft c and g

1 **Revise your spelling list from page 29.** Which list word means?

a A bacteria or virus that causes illness _____

b The son of a king _____

c 100 years _____

d To move your body to music _____

e How much something costs _____

f A symbol used to show a number _____

Challenge words

2 **Write the word.**

accident _____

genius _____

allergic _____

surgery _____

gigantic _____

message _____

celebrate _____

rejoice _____

emergency _____

announce _____

3 **Word clues.** Which challenge word means?

a very clever _____

b medical operation _____

c bad reaction _____

d a letter _____

e crisis _____

f to be full of joy _____

g very large _____

h unplanned _____

i to make known _____

4 **Complete the sentence.**

a I didn't mean to break the cup; it was an _____.

b A birthday is a good reason to _____.

c The nurses prepared the patient for _____.

d A whale is a _____ creature!

e They are about to _____ the winner of the election.

f I left my friend a secret _____.

Verbs

A **verb** is the most important word in a sentence. It can be
- a '**doing**' word; e.g., She **runs**.
- a '**being**' word; e.g., He **is** my brother.
- a '**having**' word; e.g., He **has** a cat.

1 **Fill in the verbs from the box.**

a My dog _____ a very furry coat.

b The little girl _____ very sparkly shoes.

c I _____ next to my friend at the concert.

d The spectators _____ already in the stadium.

e My mother _____ us to basketball practice.

f The carpenter _____ the nail into the wood.

g My brother _____ when he sees a mouse.

| has |
| hammers |
| sit |
| screams |
| drives |
| are |
| wears |

2 **Circle the words that show that an action is happening.**

a Harry helps his brother.

b Lily jumps for joy.

c Ling fixes her bicycle.

d Reuben washes his hair.

e Molly arranges her cards.

f Daniel walks to the library.

g The choir sings beautifully.

h The audience claps loudly.

i The pilot flies the plane.

j Mom mows the lawn on Saturdays.

3 **Choose the correct verb.**

a Their mothers (teach, teaches) _____ them how to drive.

b Esther and Cate (swim, swims) _____ a length of the pool.

c Mr. Kumar (help, helps) _____ the children with their artworks.

d The artists (display, displays) _____ their work at the gallery.

e Our little dog (gobble, gobbles) _____ all his food and then
   (want, wants) _____ more.

Sea Life

Compare and contrast
Compare and contrast information by looking for the similarities and differences between details in the text.

Read the passage.

Circle what kind of animal whales and seals are.

Highlight the reason whales and seals cannot breathe underwater.

Color what whales and seals feed their babies.

Underline where baby whales are born.

Put a box around where seal pups are born.

Underline where seals spend most of their time.

Whales, dolphins, seals, and sea lions are marine mammals.

Mammals cannot breathe under water because they have lungs, not gills. They must come to the surface to breathe.

The babies of whales and dolphins are born underwater. The mothers push the babies to the surface to take their first breath.

Seals and sea lions spend most of their time in the water, feeding on fish, squid, and penguins. They also spend time on land, resting. Seal pups are born on land and like all marine mammal babies, they are fed on milk.

Circle the correct answer/s for each question.

1 In which three ways are whales and seals **similar**?

a Both give birth to their babies on land.
b Both spend time resting on land.
c Both must come to the surface to breathe.
d Both are mammals.
e Both spend all of their time in the water.
f Both feed their babies milk.

2 In which two ways are seals **different** from whales?

a Their babies are born on land.
b They have lungs, not gills.
c They are marine mammals.
d They spend time in the water and on land.
e They spend all their time in the water.

RI.4.1 Refer to details and examples in a text when explaining what the text says explicitly and when drawing inferences from the text.

Sea Life

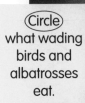

Read the full text

Sea Life

Read the passage.

Circle what wading birds and albatrosses eat.

Underline where oystercatchers live and feed.

Color how albatrosses catch their food.

Many birds depend on the sea for their food. Wading birds, penguins, albatrosses, gulls, and pelicans hunt and eat fish and other sea creatures.

Wading birds, such as oystercatchers, live and feed along the shore. Long, spindly legs help them wade through shallow water. Their thin beaks dig around for small animals in the water and mud.

Out over the deeper ocean, birds need to be able to fly for long periods of time. The albatross has very long wings so that it can glide for hours. It can stay in the air for weeks at a time. These seabirds dive into the water to catch their food.

Penguins cannot fly at all. They use their flippers and their webbed feet to swim very fast and catch fish.

Highlight how oystercatchers find their food.

Put a box around where albatrosses find their food.

Color how penguins are different from other seabirds.

1 Describe one way in which oystercatchers and albatrosses are **similar**.

_____

_____

2 Describe the **different** ways in which oystercatchers and albatrosses find their food.

_____

_____

_____

_____

3 Describe the main **difference** between albatrosses and penguins.

_____

_____

_____

Endings: le, el, al

Most two-syllable words that end in the **l sound** have the letters **le** at the end; e.g., wrink**le**.

Some two-syllable words that end in the **l** sound have the letters **el** or **al** at the end; e.g., flann**el**, therm**al**.

List   **①**   **Write the word.**

battle

eagle

metal

model

marble

noble

total

simple

handle

beetle

sprinkle

crystal

squirrel

satchel

wrinkle

shuffle

mammal

crackle

syllable

moral

② **Word clues.** Which list word matches?

a   collects acorns

b   part of a word

c   a clear rock

d   a fight

e   iron, copper, and gold

f   a small bag

③ **Rhyme time.** Which list word rhymes with?

a   duffle

b   nettle

c   coral

d   rattle

e   beagle

④ **Chunks.** Rearrange the chunks to make a list word.

a   al y st cr

b   i wr le nk

c   a le nd h

d   m b ar le

e   t ee le b

⑤ **Name.**

a _____ b _____ c _____ d _____

  L.4.2.D Spell grade-appropriate words correctly.

Endings: le, el, al

1 **Complete each sentence with a list word.**

a The _____ was collecting acorns for the winter.

b The _____ of five and seven is twelve.

c A _____ is a warm-blooded creature that gives birth to live young.

d I used my iron to flatten the deep _____ in my shirt.

e When the door _____ got stuck, I was trapped in the bathroom.

Challenge words

2 **Write the word.**

article _____

morsel _____

enamel _____

vertical _____

rural _____

grumble _____

constable _____

resemble _____

mineral _____

scoundrel _____

3 **Word clues.** Which challenge word matches?

a found in a newspaper _____

b relating to the country _____

c straight up and down _____

d covers your tooth _____

e formed in the earth _____

f British word for police officer _____

g to look alike _____

h a dishonest person _____

i to complain _____

j small piece of food _____

4 **Complete the sentence.**

a We were all so hungry there wasn't a _____ left on the plate.

b People often say that I _____ my dad.

c Many people from _____ areas are moving to bigger cities.

d I drew two _____ lines and one horizontal line.

e If you don't brush your teeth, you will damage the _____.

f The court case was featured in an _____ in the local newspaper.

g In London, we reported the theft to the _____.

Auxiliary verbs

> **Auxiliary verbs** are verbs that **help other verbs do their work**. They come **before the main verb**; e.g., They **are** walking.

1 Complete each sentence with an auxiliary verb from the box.

a I _____ try again later.

b The sun _____ shining yesterday.

c I _____ taking my dog for a walk.

d They _____ eating their lunch.

e I _____ finished all my chores.

f She _____ not know how to cook.

g He _____ looking for a book in the library.

| am |
| is |
| are |
| was |
| will |
| have |
| does |

2 Choose the correct verb.

a The singer (is/are) _____ practicing her new song.

b The children (is/are) _____ riding their bikes in the park.

c My father (has/have) _____ made apple pie for dessert.

d The children (has/have) _____ asked to go home early.

e The kitten (was/were) _____ playing with a ball of wool.

f The lifeguards (was/were) _____ patrolling the beaches.

g My friend (do, does) _____ not like going to parties.

h The actors (do, does) _____ not know their lines.

3 Match the beginnings and endings.

a The raindrops   is ticking.

b The clock   were training.

c The athletes   are falling.

4 Do or does?

a He _____ not sit next to me.

b I _____ not know how to swim.

L.4.1 Demonstrate command of the conventions of standard English grammar and usage when writing or speaking.

Polar Animals

Sequencing events
To identify the sequence of events in a text, look at numbers and words that give clues to the order in which things happen.

Read the passage.

Circle what happens just before the female goes to feed.

Highlight how long the female stays at sea.

Put a box around when the egg hatches.

Underline how the male protects the egg.

Color how long the chick stays in the brood pouch.

Emperor penguins are the only warm-blooded animals that spend winter in Antarctica.

In May, the female lays a single egg, and then walks to the sea to feed. She stays at sea until the egg hatches.

The male stays behind to look after the egg. He balances the egg on his feet and protects it under a thick roll of skin called a brood pouch. During this time, the male does not eat.

The egg hatches after about two months. The chick stays in the brood pouch until it can survive on its own.

The female returns to feed the chick. The male then leaves to find food.

Circle the correct answer for each question.

1 **When** does the female Emperor penguin go to the sea to feed?
- a after the egg hatches
- b while the egg is hatching
- c after she lays the egg
- d before she lays the egg

2 **What happens while** the female is feeding?
- a The male looks after the egg.
- b The other penguins look after the egg.
- c The male goes in search of food.
- d The male grows a brood pouch.

3 **When** does the female return from the sea?
- a just before the egg hatches
- b once the egg hatches
- c while the egg is hatching
- d once the chick can survive on its own

Polar Animals

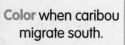

Read the passage.

Circle when caribou migrate north.

Put a box around the season that comes after spring.

Highlight what caribou do in summer.

Caribou are wild reindeer. They live in the Arctic regions of Russia, Alaska, Canada, and Greenland.

Caribou live in herds. The herd protects calves from predators such as bears, lynxes, and golden eagles.

In spring, caribou migrate about 3,000 miles north to breed on the Arctic tundra. All summer, they eat leaves and grass to build up their fat stores for winter.

When the tundra becomes cold and windy, the herds migrate south to forests. They spend winter in forests, feeding on plants such as lichens and mosses.

Color when caribou migrate south.

Underline the season that comes before spring.

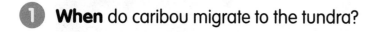

1 **When** do caribou migrate to the tundra?

_____

2 Use the information in the text to help you complete the following sentences.

During a _____ , caribou build up their fat stores for b _____ .

The herds migrate south when c _____

_____ .

During d _____ , caribou live in forests, where they feed on plants such as lichens and mosses.

When spring returns, e _____

_____ .

RI.4.8 Explain how an author uses reasons and evidence to support particular points in a text.

Ending: ge

> At the end of a word or syllable, the **j sound** is spelled **dge** if it comes after a short vowel; e.g., bri**dge**. After all other sounds, it is spelled **ge**; e.g., banda**ge**.

List

① Write the word.

stage _____

judge _____

ridge _____

lodge _____

badge _____

large _____

dodge _____

nudge _____

fudge _____

ledge _____

bridge _____

pledge _____

fridge _____

sludge _____

strange _____

grudge _____

wedge _____

smudge _____

trudge _____

budget _____

② Unscramble these list words.

a seglud _____

b ddgoe _____

c eufdg _____

d eidrg _____

e ldgee _____

f egujd _____

g drtegu _____

h elpdge _____

③ In a group. Write the list word that belongs in each group.

a stomp, plod, _____

b jab, poke, _____

c cabin, hut, _____

d shelf, platform, _____

e big, giant, _____

f odd, peculiar, _____

g stain, mark, _____

h swerve, avoid, _____

④ Name.

a _____

b _____

c _____

Ending: ge

1 **Revise your spelling list from page 39.** Underline the mistakes. Write the word correctly.

a Over Thanksgiving weekend, our frige is always full of food. _____

b I managed to doge the dirty sock my brother sent flying. _____

c I hope the juge decides to rule in our favor. _____

d We will be performing our dance routine on stagge. _____

e The cat likes to sit on the window ledje in the sunshine. _____

f We made a pledje to keep each other's secrets. _____

Challenge words

2 **Write the word.**

porridge _____

arrange _____

gadget _____

fidget _____

badger _____

cartridge _____

lodger _____

knowledge _____

language _____

average _____

3 **Word clues.** Which challenge word means?

a a British breakfast food _____

b how we communicate _____

c to move restlessly _____

d a furry animal _____

e a small container _____

f to put in order _____

g a clever or unusual device

_____

h someone who rents a room

_____

4 **Complete the sentence.**

a We went to the store to buy another ink _____ for our printer.

b On our hike we came across a _____ digging a burrow.

c Mom bought a new _____ that can make ice cream in seconds.

d My sister likes to _____, and can never sit still.

e We are having a _____ come to stay in our spare room.

f For my age, I'm above _____ height.

 L.4.2.D Spell grade-appropriate words correctly.

Progressive tense

The tense of a verb tells us when an action takes place. **Progressive tense** describes an action that **is**, **was** or **will be** happening. It has one or more auxiliary verbs before the main verb; e.g., She **is skipping**. He **was working**. They **will be running**.

1 **Fill in the missing verbs. Use each verb once.**

a We _____ a surprise party for his birthday.

b She _____ in her picture.

c He _____ on one leg.

d You _____ on my chair.

e Everyone _____ for their favorite team.

were sitting   are planning   is coloring   will be cheering   was standing

2 **Write these sentences in the past progressive tense.**

I am jumping.   I was jumping.

a She is drawing.   _____

b They are talking.   _____

c We are going.   _____

d You are trying.   _____

e It is shaking.   _____

3 **Underline the incorrect verb and write it correctly.**

a I is reading an interesting book.   _____

b I were climbing the tree when I fell.   _____

c She were showing them her new game.   _____

d He is close the window because he is cold. _____

e She will be leave for camp in the morning. _____

f They was meeting their friends at the movies. _____

Materials

Read the passage.

Drawing conclusions
To draw conclusions from a text, use clues to make your own judgments. The clues will help you find the answers that are hiding in the text.

(Circle) where sand, limestone, and soda ash are melted.

Put a box around the word that shows that glass can be used over and over.

Underline what happens to molten glass.

Glass is made by mixing sand, limestone, and soda ash in a furnace. The molten glass is poured into a mold or laid out in sheets. It hardens as it cools.

Glass breaks easily. This property can be changed by adding chemicals or by changing the way glass cools. If you reheat glass, then quickly cool it, the glass becomes much stronger.

Pyrex glass is a special type of glass. It does not expand when it is heated as much as normal glass.

Glass can be recycled over and over again.

Circle the correct answer for each question.

1 Which is the best **conclusion**? Glass is made by melting a mixture of minerals at …
   a low temperatures.   b freezing temperatures.   c very high temperatures.

2 Which is the best **clue** to question 1's answer?
   a poured   b furnace   c mold   d sheets

3 Which is the best **conclusion**? Glass can be made into …
   a one shape only.   b flat shapes only.
   c long shapes only.   d lots of different shapes.

4 Which two words are the best **clues** to question 3's answer?
   a *mold* and *sheets*   b *sand* and *limestone*
   c *hardens* and *cools*   d *mixing* and *poured*

5 Which is the best **conclusion**? Glass …
   a is an eco-friendly material.   b is harmful to the environment.
   c has very few uses.   d is a very soft material.

Materials

Read the full text

Materials

Read the passage.

Circle the different ways of collecting metals from ores.

Highlight what makes iron and steel corrode faster.

Most metals come from minerals. Rocks that contain minerals are called ores. They are crushed or heated to collect the metal.

Iron comes from iron ore. It is made into steel by adding carbon.

Metals can corrode. When rust eats away at iron or steel, it corrodes. Rust is a flaky, brown substance that forms when oxygen, water, and iron combine. This process is faster if the water is salty.

An alloy is a mixture of metals. For example, stainless steel is an alloy of steel and chromium. Alloys have different properties. They can be stronger, lighter, and softer than other metals.

Underline how iron ore is changed into steel.

Put a box around what is added to steel to make stainless steel.

1. The text **suggests** that there are different ways of collecting metals from ores. Which words are the **clues**?

_____

2. Why can we **conclude** that iron and steel will corrode faster in sea water?

_____

_____

_____

3. Why can we **conclude** that steel and stainless steel have different properties?

_____

_____

_____

_____

Suffix: ed

If a verb ends in a consonant that has a <u>short vowel before</u> it, **double the consonant** before adding **ed**; e.g., si**p** → si**pp**ed.

List ① Write the word.

mapped _____

begged _____

sipped _____

spotted _____

tugged _____

gripped _____

pinned _____

skipped _____

stabbed _____

tanned _____

flipped _____

quizzed _____

swapped _____

thinned _____

cropped _____

skinned _____

shipped _____

trotted _____

stemmed _____

knotted _____

② Chunks. Rearrange the chunks to make a list word.

a nn a ed t _____

b ed nn i sk _____

c a pp ed m _____

d i pp s ed _____

e i pp gr ed _____

f e gg b ed _____

g u gg ed t _____

h nn p i ed _____

③ In a group. Write the list word that belongs in each group.

a questioned, asked, _____

b gulped, swallowed, _____

c pulled, heaved, _____

d tossed, flicked, _____

e tied, tangled, _____

f requested, pleaded, _____

g hopped, jumped, _____

h traded, exchanged, _____

④ Fill in the missing letters.

a gr_____

b ski_____

c cro_____

d kn_____

e ste_____

f t__g_____

⑤ Unscramble these list words.

a ppedski _____

b pproced _____

c mmedets _____

d onttdek _____

e oedttps _____

f papdem _____

L.4.2.D Spell grade-appropriate words correctly.

Suffix: ed

1 **Revise your spelling list from page 44.** Underline the mistakes.
Write the word correctly.

a   Mom pined the hem of my dress.   _____

b   I croped the picture so it would fit the frame.   _____

c   Instead of walking to the park, we skiped together.   _____

d   The adventurers maped out the course ahead.   _____

e   The horse troted around the field.   _____

f   I fliped through the pages of the book.   _____

Challenge words

2 **Write the word.**

strapped   _____

shunned   _____

quipped   _____

throbbed   _____

allotted   _____

overlapped   _____

equipped   _____

boycotted   _____

clogged   _____

omitted   _____

3 **Hidden words.** Find the challenge word.

a   ppedquippedquip   _____

b   ppedequippedequi   _____

c   cottboycottedbpoy   _____

d   ttedomittedomit   _____

e   sfsdshunnedfgvds   _____

f   sddfgfvsthrobbedg   _____

g   dfcloggeddfsdfgsd   _____

h   dgvdstrappedfsfdf   _____

i   dfdeallotteddfdttv   _____

j   pedoverlappedarre   _____

4 **Complete the sentence.**

a   The roof tiles _____ each other.

b   The singers were _____ ten minute each to perform.

c   My finger _____ after I jammed it in the door.

d   The sink was overflowing because the drain was _____.

e   I _____ my knee and elbow pads on before going skating.

f   He was _____ by his friends for being rude.

Commas in lists

Commas (,) separate items in a list; e.g., We saw orangutans, lions, and tigers.

1 **Fill in the commas.**

a   Mom handed out backpacks compasses and maps.

b   You can read a book a magazine or the newspaper.

c   Sam can play the flute the violin and the piano.

d   I put my towel T-shirt shorts and socks into the laundry basket.

e   The box contained a yellow ribbon a silver buckle and an old coin.

f   I watered the plants swept the drive and took the dog for a walk.

2 **Check (✔) the sentence that has the correct punctuation.**

a   Every, afternoon they play basketball baseball or soccer.

b   In olden days, there were no cars, phones or computers.

c   Through the window I could see trees, flowers, and bushes.

d   The children planted carrots, pumpkins and potatoes.

3 **Correct each sentence.**

a   At the market, we bought bread, milk and vegetables.

b   Amazingly, he has never eaten pizza, pasta, hamburgers or doughnuts.

c   From the top of the building, we could see the sea mountains, and farmland.

d   Because I was sick, I couldn't visit Grandma on Monday Tuesday or Wednesday.

4 **Write a sentence with each list.**

a   *paint, pencils, crayons* _____

_____

b   *whales, tigers, rhinos* _____

L.4.2 Demonstrate command of the conventions of standard English punctuation when writing.

Spelling

Use this review to test your knowledge. It has three parts—**Spelling**, **Grammar**, and **Comprehension**. If you're unsure of an answer, go back and read the rules and generalizations in the blue boxes.

You have learned about:

- long vowel sounds
- suffix: ing
- endings: le, el, al
- digraphs: ew, ue, ui
- plurals: s, es
- ending: ge
- trigraphs: air, eer, ear
- soft c and g
- suffix: ed

1 **In each sentence, the spelling error has been <u>underlined</u>. Write the correct spelling.** 2 marks

   a "Yum! This chocolate mousse has a delightful creamy <u>tayst</u>."   _____

   b Next year I'm learning to play the <u>floote</u>.   _____

   c Dad <u>threuw</u> cashews and dried fruit together to make a trail mix.   _____

   d The fire brigade worked hard to <u>reskew</u> the family.   _____

2 **Which word correctly completes this sentence?** 1 mark

   We're _____ a surprise party for Dad's 40th birthday.

   a planned   b plan   c plans   d planning

3 **Which word correctly completes this sentence?** 1 mark

   George Washington and Martin Luther King Jr. were great _____.

   a leaders   b leading   c leads   d leader

4 **This sentence has one word that is incorrect. Write the correct spelling.** 1 mark

   You can always find fresh fruit and vegetables in our frige.   _____

5 **Write the sounds air, eer, or ear to correctly complete these words.** 1 mark

   a p __ __ __ l   b __ __ __ ie   c pr __ __ __ ie

6 **Circle the correct verb to complete each sentence.** 2 marks

   a Alex slowly (sip, sipping, sipped) his strawberry milkshake.

   b On safari I (spot, spotting, spotted) a lion, a giraffe, and a herd of elephants.

   c The children were (grin, grinning, grinned) at the pet shop window.

   d The cows were (whip, whipping, whipped) their tails to keep away flies.

7 **This sentence has one word that is incorrect. Write the correct spelling.** 1 mark

   The Japanese spider crab is a jigantic creature.   _____

8 **Complete these words with le, el, or al.** 1 mark

   a batt __ __   b tot __ __   c squirr __ __

Your score

☐

10

Grammar

You have learned about:

- common and proper nouns
- writing titles
- auxiliary verbs
- capital letters
- pronouns
- progressive tense
- common and abstract nouns
- verbs
- commas in lists

1 **In each sentence, color the common noun and underline the proper noun.** 2 marks

a We're going to the beach on Sunday.

b They're going to visit their cousins in Italy.

c The next train does not stop in Houston.

d I asked Jerome to come with me to the park.

2 **In the following sentences, underline the words that need capital letters.** 2 marks

a The longest rivers in the world are the amazon and the nile.

b The capital city of japan is tokyo.

c The grand canyon is a popular tourist attraction in arizona.

d My favorite months of the year are july and august.

3 **Color the common nouns and underline the abstract nouns.** 3 marks

child	power	crime
childhood	powder	criminal

4 **Write the following book titles with the correct capitalization.** 2 marks

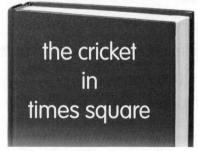

the cricket
in
times square

the beginning
of
everything

a _____

_____

b _____

_____

Grammar

5 **In the following sentences, replace the words in parentheses with pronouns.** 2 marks

   a   I watched (Max and Molly) _____ digging in the garden.

   b   (Max and Molly) _____ were looking for a bone.

   c   Max had hidden (the bone) _____ in one of the flower beds.

   d   Max and Molly were spraying sand all over (Max and Molly) _____.

6 **In each sentence, underline the verbs.** 3 marks

   a   The keys are on the table where I put them last night.

   b   The little girl smiled when she saw her father.

   c   My friend has a cute dog that follows him everywhere.

7 **In the following sentences, fill in the missing auxiliary verbs.** 2 marks

   a   Right now the children _____ playing outside.

   b   When we saw him yesterday, he _____ waiting for the bus.

   c   Today I _____ going to take the book back to the library.

   d   They _____ eating dinner when they heard the explosion.

8 **Write the following sentences in the progressive tense.** 2 marks

   a   Dominic collects old coins. _____

      _____

   b   Our dog ran around the garden. _____

      _____

9 **Complete each sentence with a list of FOUR items.** 2 marks

   a   My favorite fruits are _____

      _____

   b   At the shops I bought _____

      _____

Your
score

  ☐

20

One Minute Past Midnight

Read the passage and then use the comprehension skills you have learned to answer the questions.

Samuel awoke with a start. Except for a thin sliver of light that shone through a crack in the curtains, his room was dark and still. The luminous hands of his bedside clock read one minute past midnight. What was it that had woken him? Samuel sat up in bed, his body tense, and listened intently. At first there was nothing but the sound of his ragged breathing. Then he heard it — a faint clicking sound, neither loud nor soft. Very quietly, Samuel got out of bed and crept out to the hallway, eerily lit by a waning moon. He paused, head tilted to one side. He could just hear the sound — click, click, click — above the loud thumping of his heart. It seemed to be coming from the study at the end of the hall. Samuel stole cautiously towards the closed door. With trembling fingers, he took hold of the knob and turned it slowly. Gently he nudged the door open.

A patch of moonlight lit up the faded carpet on the floor. Samuel peered into the gloom. The sound was coming from a dark corner of the room. He fumbled for the light switch and snapped it on. Light flooded the room and a wave of relief swept over Samuel when he saw what was causing the clicking sound. His father must have forgotten to switch off the fan. One of the blades was bent and each time it spun around, it hit the guard, making a clicking noise. The tension drained from Samuel's body as he strode across the room and switched off the fan. Satisfied that he had taken care of the problem, he turned off the light and left the study.

Samuel stepped back into the hall and headed towards his room. Suddenly he stopped. The hairs on the back of his neck rose. There was that noise again. Click, click, click. But this time, it was coming from his room!

1 What woke Samuel? 1 mark   **LITERAL**

   a light coming through the curtains   **b** his noisy breathing

   c a clicking sound   **d** his alarm clock

One Minute Past Midnight

2 How did Samuel feel as he walked towards the study? 1 mark · INFERENTIAL

a excited
b curious
c annoyed
d scared

3 Give a text clue to support your answer to question 2. 2 marks · CRITICAL

_____

_____

4 In this text, what does the word 'stole' mean? 1 mark · VOCABULARY

a moved quietly
b robbed
c snatched
d stumbled

5 Which group of words tells you that Samuel was nervous about entering the study? 1 mark · INFERENTIAL

a took hold of
b turned it slowly
c with trembling fingers
d nudged the door open

6 What does the word 'strode' suggest about the way Samuel walked? It suggests that Samuel walked ... 1 mark · INFERENTIAL

a slowly.
b confidently.
c hesitantly.
d on tiptoes.

7 What is the main purpose of this text? 1 mark · CRITICAL

a to remind readers to switch off their fans
b to entertain readers
c to explain how fans work
d to describe a character

8 Explain why the hairs on the back of Samuel's neck rose. 2 marks · CRITICAL

_____

_____

Your score

☐

10

Click Click Click Click

Your Review 1 Scores

Spelling		Grammar		Comprehension		Total
☐	+	☐	+	☐	=	☐
10		20		10		40

Feral and Spam

Point of view
To identify point of view, look at the way characters act and feel. The clues are in the way they express their opinions and views (what they think and feel).

Read the passage.

Put a box around the narrator's name.

Circle how Fairlie feels about being a twin.

Highlight pronouns that show who is telling the story.

I hate being a twin. I guess it might be OK if you were an identical twin. You could fool other people by pretending you were the other twin. But Sam and I only got the bad bits of being a twin—like having to share our birthday. That was a real drag.

"I'm not having a party with all of his friends there," I yelled.

"Now Fairlie," Mom began in her best 'don't-argue-with-me' voice, "I'm not having two separate birthday parties. I don't see why you make so much fuss about this."

Circle the correct answer for each question.

1 From Fairlie's **point of view**, what is one of the worst things about being a twin?

   a swapping identities   b sharing identities

   c sharing birthdays   d sharing chores

2 Which phrase is the best **clue** to question 1's answer?

   a having a party   b a real drag   c Sam and I   d the other twin

3 From whose **point of view** is the passage written?

   a Fairlie's   b Sam's   c Mom's   d a friend's

4 Which pronouns helped you answer question 3?

   a *you* and *your*   b *he* and *his*   c *I* and *our*   d *they* and *them*

5 Which word shows that Mom **thinks** Fairlie is overreacting?

   a separate   b parties   c birthday   d fuss

RL.4.1 Refer to details and examples in a text when explaining what the text says explicitly and when drawing inferences from the text.

Feral and Spam

Read the
whole story

Feral and Spam

by Bev McGregor
Illustrated by Alex Frank

Read the passage.

Color what Mom
threatened to do.

"Perhaps I should just organize a party for Sam this year," Mom threatened.

"Yeah. Perhaps there should just be a party for Sam," Sam agreed.

"Fine," I said. "Suits me. Sam can have his party this year and I'll have mine next year."

Sam didn't look quite so happy with that idea. Mom did though.

"What a wonderful idea, Fairlie," she said.

"Wonderful," Sam said without enthusiasm.

Underline what
Mom thought of
Fairlie's idea.

Put a box
around how Sam
said "Wonderful".

1 What did Mom **think** of Fairlie's idea?

_____

_____

2 How did Sam **feel** when Mom suggested that this year's party be just for him?

_____

_____

_____

3 How did Sam's **feelings** change when Fairlie suggested that they take turns in having a party?

_____

_____

_____

4 Which phrase suggests that Sam did not really **think** that Fairlie's idea was so wonderful?

_____

_____

Prefixes: un, dis, mis

> Adding the **prefix un**, **dis**, or **mis** to a word usually turns it into its opposite; e.g., **un**wise, **dis**like, **mis**lead.

List

unhappy
unclear
dislike
misfit
uneasy
unwilling
mislaid
dislodge
disown
unstable
unlawful
discount
disorder
mismatch
misunderstood
unchanged
disregard
disinfect
disloyal
dismount

1 **Write the word.**

_____
_____
_____
_____
_____
_____
_____
_____
_____
_____
_____
_____
_____
_____
_____
_____
_____
_____
_____
_____

2 **Missing prefix.** Write the missing prefix.

a _____happy
b _____changed
c _____understood
d _____clear
e _____regard
f _____lodge
g _____willing
h _____lawful
i _____stable
j _____order
k _____like
l _____easy
m _____laid
n _____fit
o _____match
p _____mount

3 **Chunks.** Rearrange the letters to make a list word.

a ga dis rd re _____
b or dis der _____
c fi t mis _____
d law un ful _____
e mo dis t un _____
f la mis id _____
g al loy dis _____
h sta le un b _____

4 **Sort the words.**

un	mis	dis

L.4.2.D Spell grade-appropriate words correctly.

Prefixes: un, dis, mis

1 **Revise your spelling list from page 54.** Underline the spelling mistakes. Write the word correctly.

a It was disclear how we would get there. _____

b I mislike eating Brussels sprouts. _____

c The weather report remained mischanged. _____

d Tan has unlaid his cell phone. _____

e Mom would misinfect the bench after cooking. _____

f When Tilly was dishappy, she would cry. _____

g Fabian was diswilling to go to bed. _____

h I had disunderstood the question. _____

Challenge words

2 **Write the word.**

unpopular _____

disjointed _____

disadvantage _____

misadventure _____

disqualify _____

uncommon _____

discontented _____

unsatisfactory _____

discomfort _____

misfortune _____

3 **Hidden words.** Find the challenge words.

a dxsddisqualifydfd _____

b gdxuncommonfg _____

c dunsatisfactorydf _____

d dffgunpopularfgf _____

e gvfdisadvantaged _____

f fdfdiscontenteddf _____

g sefdisjointedgvds _____

h dgvfdiscomfortxf _____

i nemisfortunemis _____

j vemisadventuretre _____

4 **Complete the sentence.**

a Missing soccer practice meant Dan was at a _____.

b I hoped that would not _____ me from the competition.

c Rain is _____ at this time of year.

d Mom gave me more medicine to ease my _____.

e Chores are very _____ with children.

Adjective order

Adjectives describe **nouns** or **pronouns**. A noun may have two or three adjectives in front of it. They should appear in the following **order**:
- first, adjectives that give an **opinion**; e.g., good, delicious
- secondly, adjectives that **describe**; e.g., sweet, creamy
- thirdly, adjectives that give the **kind or type** of something; e.g., birthday.

1 **Fill in the adjectives.**

| old | wooden | mountain | cute | iron | black | cotton |

a My friend has a _____ little Burmese kitten.

b I told him to wash his dirty white _____ socks.

c The lady was wearing a smart _____ woollen coat.

d The pirate grabbed hold of the rusty old _____ handle.

e We entered the hall through a fantastic red _____ door.

f His parents gave him an amazing new _____ bike for his birthday.

g I saw an _____ gray African elephant at the zoo.

2 **Write the underlined adjectives in the right order.**

a an <u>red ugly plastic</u> mug   _____

b a <u>silk beautiful pink</u> dress   _____

c a <u>smart cotton white</u> shirt   _____

d a <u>green pretty glass</u> bead   _____

e a <u>old leather comfortable</u> chair   _____

f an <u>wooden round unusual</u> table   _____

g a <u>horrible metal yellow</u> frame   _____

3 **Circle the adjectives that can describe the sword and the cheetah.**

a
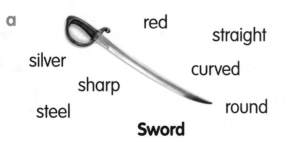
red   straight   silver   curved   sharp   steel   round

Sword

b
striped   wild   fast   slow   green   strong   spotted

Cheetah

L.4.1.D Order adjectives within sentences according to conventional patterns.

Isabella

Cause and effect
To find cause and effect, ask why something happens and what the result is.

Read the passage.

Highlight the object Toby tripped over.

Underline the reason Toby dug through the sand.

Circle the object that was buried in the sand.

Color what was clinging to the bell.

Put a box around the date on the bell.

Toby climbed down the stairs to the beach. He looked out across the sea as he walked. Suddenly, Toby tripped over something and fell face first into the sand.

Toby stood up and brushed the wet sand from his clothes. He bent down for a closer look at what he had tripped on.

It was a piece of wood. As Toby lifted it, something underneath caught his eye. He dug through the sand and uncovered a bell. Toby lifted the bell and scraped off the barnacles. There was a date carved on its side.

"1892," Toby read.

Circle the correct answer for each question.

1 What **caused** Toby to trip?

  a a bell   b a broken stair   c a hole in the sand   d a piece of wood

2 What **caused** Toby to dig through the sand? He ...

  a saw something.   b felt something.   c heard something.   d smelled something.

3 What **happened** when Toby dug through the sand? He found ...

  a some barnacles.   b a bell.   c a piece of wood.   d an old box.

4 What is the most likely **reason** the bell was covered in barnacles? It had once been ...

  a on a boat.   b in the ocean.   c on a rock.   d on dry land.

5 What **happens** when barnacles come in contact with a hard surface? They ...

  a try to eat it.   b swim around it.   c attach themselves to it.   d play with it.

Isabella

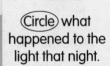

Read the whole story

Read the passage.

Put a box around the date in the diary.

Highlight who wrote the diary entry.

Color the reason the lighthouse keeper fell asleep.

Circle what happened to the light that night.

Underline what happened to *The Isabella*.

Felix Thompson was seated at the table.

Felix stood and looked at Toby. "I'm sorry about before." Then he handed Toby a black book. "This is my great-grandfather's diary. It tells all about the night of October 12, 1892."

Toby was stunned. He opened the lighthouse keeper's diary and read. "It has been a bad week. Storm, after storm, after storm. I was dead on my feet. Fell asleep on watch. The light must have gone out during the night. I didn't know any damage had been done until the next day. When I heard that *The Isabella* was missing in my waters, I lied when I filled in the logbook."

1 **Why** did Felix's great-grandfather fall asleep on the night of October 12, 1892?

_____

_____

2 What **happened as a result** of Felix's great-grandfather falling asleep that night?

_____

_____

_____

3 What is the most likely **reason** that Felix's great-grandfather lied when he filled in the logbook?

_____

_____

RL.4.1 Refer to details and examples in a text when explaining what the text says explicitly and when drawing inferences from the text.

Plurals: s, ies

> If a noun ends in **y** and there is a **consonant before it**, change the **y** to **i** and add **es**; e.g. ar**my** → arm**ies**.
> If a noun ends in **y** and there is a **vowel before it**, add **s** to make it plural; e.g., d**ay** → d**ays**.

List ① **Write the word.**

entries _____

chimneys _____

relays _____

diaries _____

supplies _____

valleys _____

donkeys _____

displays _____

replies _____

worries _____

industries _____

memories _____

activities _____

groceries _____

centuries _____

kidneys _____

holidays _____

factories _____

charities _____

remedies _____

② **Name.**

a _____ b _____

③ **In a group.** Write the list word that belongs in each group.

a horses, mules, _____

b answers, responses, _____

c years, decades, _____

d medicines, vaccines, _____

e intestines, lungs, _____

f journals, records, _____

g shows, exhibits, _____

h vents, fireplaces, _____

④ **Word clues.** Which list word matches?

a you bring these home from the market _____

b photographs bring them back _____

c animals that look similar to horses _____

d Labor Day, Memorial Day, Independence Day _____

e smoke comes out of these _____

f things that heal you when you are sick _____

Plurals: s, ies

1 Revise your spelling list from page 59. Fill in the missing letters.

a entr_____
b repla_____
c suppl_____
d displa_____
e worr_____
f industr_____
g holida_____

2 Chunks. Rearrange the chunks to make a list word.

a tr ies in dus _____
b tur ies cen _____
c im ys ch ne _____
d cer gro ies _____
e tor fac ies _____
f ays dis pl _____
g dies rem e _____

Challenge words

3 Write the word.

categories _____
abbeys _____
properties _____
pulleys _____
ceremonies _____
mysteries _____
qualities _____
strategies _____
societies _____
convoys _____

4 Word clues. Which challenge word means?

a simple machines used for lifting
_____
b religious places or buildings
_____
c special occasions
_____
d something secret or unknown
_____
e communities or groups
_____
f vehicles or ships that travel together
_____

5 Complete the sentence.

a I divided my doll collection into _____.
b We raised the curtain using a series of _____.
c The award _____ all take place in the great hall.
d The church _____ raised money for charity.
e The basketball team worked out their game _____.

L.4.2.D Spell grade-appropriate words correctly.

Adverbs

An **adverb** **adds meaning** to a **verb**. It tells:
- **how** something is done (manner); e.g., She **speaks** clearly.
- **when or how often** something is done (time); e.g., It's **coming** soon. We **eat** chocolate occasionally.
- **where** something is done (place); e.g., **Sit** here.

1 **Does the underlined adverb tell how, when, how often, or where?**

a We are playing <u>outside</u>. _____

b She treated them <u>kindly</u>. _____

c I told them <u>immediately</u>. _____

d The sun shone <u>brightly</u>. _____

e They <u>seldom</u> watch TV. _____

f They are waiting <u>inside</u>. _____

g I will speak to him <u>later</u>. _____

2 **Sort the adverbs.**

| sometimes | neatly | earlier | somewhere | nearby | now |
| tomorrow | daily | easily | always | hurriedly | there |

a **How?**	b **When?**	c **How often?**	d **Where?**

3 **Fill in the adverbs.**

a I _____ wake up at six o'clock.

b Our team is playing _____ this week.

c The water flowed _____ over the rocks.

d She was able to answer all the questions _____.

e There was _____ for the passengers to sit.

f I will be seeing him either _____ or tomorrow.

away

correctly

always

tonight

rapidly

nowhere

Two Old Crows

Read the passage.

Circle where the crows sat.

Highlight the words that tell how the crows talked.

Color all the words that tell what the crows thought about.

Underline the question the crow asked.

> Two old crows sat on a fence rail.
> Two old crows sat on a fence rail,
> Thinking of effect and cause,
> Of weeds and flowers,
> And nature's laws.
> One of them muttered, one of them stuttered,
> One of them stuttered, one of them muttered.
> Each of them thought far more than he uttered.
> One crow asked the other crow a riddle.
> One crow asked the other crow a riddle:
> The muttering crow
> Asked the stuttering crow,
> "Why does a bee have a sword to his fiddle?"

Circle the correct answer for each question.

1 In the passage, what is the **first** thing the two old crows do?
  a fly to a fence
  b sit on a fence
  c think about nature
  d talk to each other

2 What do the two old crows do **after** thinking of effect and cause? They think of ...
  a trees and bushes.
  b grass and seeds.
  c rivers and streams.
  d weeds and flowers.

3 In the passage, what is the **last thing** that happens?
  a One of the crows asks a riddle.
  b One of the crows answers a riddle.
  c One of the crows starts to mutter.
  d One of the crows starts to stutter.

RL.4.1 Refer to details and examples in a text when explaining what the text says explicitly and when drawing inferences from the text.

Two Old Crows

Read the passage.

Circle where the crows were sitting when they heard the bee.

Color the last thing the crows did.

Underline what happened just after the crows heard the bee.

"Why does a bee have a sword to his fiddle?"

"Bee-cause," said the other crow,

"Bee-cause,

B B B B B B B B B B B B B B B B-cause."

Just then a bee flew close to their rail:

"Buzzzzzzzzzzzzzzzzz   zzzzzzzz

zzzzzzzzzzzzzz   ZZZZZZZ."

And those two black crows

Turned pale,

And away those crows did sail.

Why?

B B B B B B B B B B B B B B B B-cause.

B B B B B B B B B B B B B B B B-cause.

"Buzzzzzzzzzzzzzzzzz   zzzzzzzz

zzzzzzzzzzzzzz ZZZZZZZ."

1 Complete the following sentences.

Two black crows were sitting on a **a** _____. Suddenly they heard

b _____

_____.

When they heard the bee, **c** _____

_____.

They were scared the bee would sting them, so **d** _____

_____.

Endings: ice, ise, ize

In words that end in **ice**, **i** can make a **short** or **long** sound and **ce** makes a **s** sound; e.g., just**ice**, dev**ice**. In most words that end in **ise** or **ize** **i** makes a **long** sound and **se** makes a **z** sound; e.g., surpr**ise**, real**ize**. In some words that end in **ise**, **i** has a **short** sound and **se** makes a **s** sound; e.g., prom**ise**.

List   **1** **Write the word.**

notice   _____

office   _____

advise   _____

justice   _____

advice   _____

police   _____

promise   _____

device   _____

practice   _____

surprise   _____

realize   _____

precise   _____

hospice   _____

novice   _____

exercise   _____

prejudice   _____

solstice   _____

supervise   _____

organize   _____

advertise   _____

2 **Sort the words.**

a ice

_____   _____

_____   _____

_____   _____

_____   _____

_____   _____

_____

b ise

_____   _____

_____   _____

_____   _____

_____   _____

c ize

_____

3 **Meaning.** Which list word means?

a A person with little or no experience   _____

b Unfair treatment toward a person or group   _____

c To be in charge of something   _____

d Repeating an activity to build skill   _____

e Exact and accurate   _____

f To give advice or recommend   _____

Endings: ice, ise, ize

1 **Revise your spelling list from page 64.** Complete each sentence with a list word.

a You should _____ regularly to stay fit and healthy.

b I like to _____ my clothes by color and size.

c Stores are beginning to _____ their holiday sales.

d I hoped people would _____ my new haircut.

e We made a _____ to keep in touch.

f I had to add the _____ amount of sugar to the recipe.

g My mom must _____ my younger sister when she uses scissors.

Challenge words

2 **Write the word.**

sacrifice _____

criticize _____

edifice _____

lattice _____

accomplice _____

precipice _____

visualize _____

emphasize _____

apprentice _____

cowardice _____

3 **Word clues.** Which challenge word means?

a a large building _____

b a steep cliff _____

c a person assisting crime

_____

d lacking courage _____

e to judge _____

f a student _____

g support for climbing plants

_____

h to give particular attention to

_____

4 **Complete the sentence.**

a The grapevine grew up the wooden _____.

b I tried to _____ what I would look like in the future.

c My dad likes to _____ the importance of chores.

d The police knew the burglar must have an _____.

e My brother works as a chef's _____.

f I hoped the judge would not _____ my performance.

Adjectives and adverbs

An **adjective** gives **information** about a **noun** or **pronoun**; e.g., The **red ball** is in the **tall cupboard**.

An **adverb** adds **meaning to a verb** by telling how, when, how often, or where something is done; e.g., **Talk** slowly. **Do** it now. **Check** it hourly. **Sit** there.

1 **Choose the correct word in parentheses to complete each sentence.**

a   This chair is very (comfortable, comfortably) _____.

b   He was sitting (comfortable, comfortably) _____ on his favorite chair.

c   The king treated his subjects (cruel, cruelly) _____.

d   The people were scared of the (cruel, cruelly) _____ king.

e   Some of the sums were (easy, easily) _____ to do.

f   My cat can (easy, easily) _____ jump over that wall.

2 **Underline the word that is wrong and write it correctly.**

a   The kitten's fur is very softly.   _____

b   He crossed the road cautious.   _____

c   The fans cheered loud for their team.   _____

d   The child is honestly and would never lie.   _____

e   The blue whale is enormously.   _____

f   She wise decided to stay indoors during the storm.   _____

3 **Is the underlined word an adjective or an adverb?**

a   I was <u>glad</u> when I heard he had made the team.   _____

b   They accepted the donation <u>gratefully</u>.   _____

c   He told them <u>repeatedly</u> to stop talking.   _____

d   The Apple Festival is an <u>annual</u> event.   _____

e   She tied the belt <u>loosely</u> around her waist.   _____

f   This is the <u>perfect</u> tool for the job.   _____

g   We were <u>miserable</u> after we lost the match.   _____

h   My brother ran <u>fast</u> and won the race.   _____

L.4.1 Demonstrate command of the conventions of standard English grammar and usage when writing or speaking.

Two Brothers, Two Rewards

Interpreting character behavior, feelings, and motivation

To interpret a character's feelings and why they act in a certain way, look for clues in the text. The clues are usually in the words and punctuation.

Read the passage.

Underline how the younger brother was different from his older brother.

Highlight what the younger brother did when he found the injured sparrow.

There were once two brothers who were very different from each other. The older brother, though rich, always wanted more. The younger brother was not rich, but he was happy with what he had.

One day the younger brother found a sparrow with a broken wing. He took it home and nursed it back to health. When it was time for the sparrow to fly away, it said, "You showed me great kindness, yet expected nothing in return. Please take this pumpkin seed. Plant it in your garden and wait for it to ripen."

When the pumpkins ripened, they contained gold, silver, and diamonds.

Color the reason the sparrow rewarded the younger brother.

Put a box around the younger brother's reward.

Circle the correct answer/s for each question.

1 What is the **most likely reason** the younger brother took care of the injured sparrow?
- a He felt sorry for the sparrow.
- b He expected the sparrow to reward him.
- c He wanted the sparrow as a pet.
- d He wanted to sell the sparrow.

2 Which adjective **best describes** the younger brother?
- a greedy
- b rich
- c caring
- d curious

3 Which **two phrases** in the passage are the clues to question 2's answer?
- a took it home
- b great kindness
- c fly away
- d nursed it

4 What is the **most likely reason** the sparrow rewarded the younger brother? The sparrow was ...
- a angry with the younger brother.
- b grateful to the younger brother.
- c scared of the younger brother.
- d feeling generous.

RL.4.3 Describe in depth a character, setting, or event in a story or drama, drawing on specific details in the text.

Two Brothers, Two Rewards

Read the passage.

Circle the reason the older brother wanted the sparrow to get better quickly.

Put a box around the reward the sparrow gave the older brother.

Color what happened when the older brother got to the top of the vine.

News of his brother's sudden fortune reached the older brother. When he heard what had happened, he took out a slingshot, shot a sparrow, and broke its wing. He took the bird home and nursed it while thinking, "The sooner you are better, the sooner I get my reward."

When the bird was better, it gave the older brother a pumpkin seed. The seed sprouted into a vine, but the vine did not grow along the ground—it grew up into the sky. "I shall climb the vine and collect my reward," said the older brother.

He climbed the vine all the way to the moon. As soon as he stepped onto the moon, the vine disappeared.

1. Explain **why** the older brother nursed the sparrow.

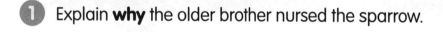

_____

_____

2. How do you think the sparrow **felt** when the older brother broke its wing?

_____

_____

3. Do you **think** the older brother got the reward he deserved? Give reasons.

_____

_____

_____

RL.4.3 Describe in depth a character, setting, or event in a story or drama, drawing on specific details in the text.

Suffixes: er, est

When we compare two nouns, we often add **er** to an adjective; e.g., long**er**. When we compare MORE than two nouns, we often add the suffix **est** to an adjective; e.g., great**est**.

If the adjective **ends in a consonant** that has a **short vowel before** it, **double the consonant** before adding **er** or **est**; e.g., fi**tt**er, fi**tt**est.

If the adjective ends in **y**, change the **y** to **i** before adding **er** or **est**; e.g., happ**y** → happ**i**er → happ**i**est.

List

1 Write the word.

faster _____

smaller _____

broadest _____

proudest _____

calmer _____

bravest _____

shorter _____

youngest _____

warmest _____

stronger _____

earlier _____

cleverer _____

ugliest _____

angriest _____

lazier _____

silliest _____

fancier _____

quieter _____

happiest _____

noisier _____

2 Opposites. Find the opposite.

a larger _____

b weaker _____

c later _____

d slower _____

e taller _____

f coldest _____

g louder _____

h saddest _____

i narrowest _____

j oldest _____

3 Name.

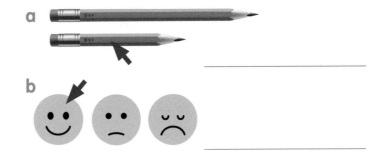

a _____

b _____

4 Fill in the table.

fast	faster	fastest
early		earliest
	happier	
short		
		proudest
strong		

Suffixes: er, est

1 **Revise your spelling list from page 69.** Add suffixes to build words.

a broad

–er _____

–est _____

b angry

–er _____

–est _____

c fancy

–er _____

–est _____

d ugly

–er _____

–est _____

e lazy

–er _____

–est _____

f fast

–er _____

–est _____

Challenge words

2 **Write the word.**

clumsier   _____

liveliest   _____

scrawniest   _____

stickier   _____

straightest   _____

looser   _____

greasiest   _____

drearier   _____

glossiest   _____

lonelier   _____

3 **Hidden words.** Find the challenge word.

a lierlonelierlone   _____

b sierclumsierclum   _____

c niestscrawniests   _____

d liestliveliestlive   _____

e dfdlooserdfgd   _____

f dfstraightestdgr   _____

g fgdfgstickierfgdf   _____

h deglossiestkiolf   _____

i rierdrearierdreer   _____

j siestgreasiestgas   _____

4 **Complete the sentence.**

a Her new puppy has the _____ coat.

b We had the _____ burgers for dinner.

c These jeans feel _____ than my old ones.

d Use this tape; it is _____ than that one.

e We had a competition to see who could draw the _____ line.

f Today is _____ than yesterday.

g We fed the _____ kitten from the bottle.

L.4.2.D Spell grade-appropriate words correctly.

Determiners

A **determiner** can be :
- an **article** (a, an, the)
- a **number adjective** (e.g., one, three, some, many, first)
- a word that **points out a specific noun** (this, that, these, those)
- a **possessive pronoun** (my, our, your, his, her, its, their)

A determiner comes **before** a **common noun**. In a sentence, a singular noun must have a determiner in front of it; e.g., **The bird** is sitting in **a tree**.

1 **Complete each sentence with a determiner from the box.**

a She is eating _____ apple.

b I let him use _____ surfboard.

c Do _____ books belong to you?

d They said we could meet at _____ house.

e I like _____ hat. Which one do you like?

f _____ athletes can run faster than others.

g Not _____ people have a pet crocodile.

| these |
| many |
| an |
| some |
| my |
| their |
| this |

2 **Match the determiner to the picture.**   an   my   four   that

a _____ cows   b _____ apple   c _____ dog   d _____ teddy

3 **Underline the mistake and write the word correctly.**

a I counted fifth stars in the sky.   _____

b Where did you buy that shoes?   _____

c Our team finished in three place.   _____

d I wiped up the mess with an cloth.   _____

e There are any animals that live in trees.   _____

f I added much water to make the mixture thinner.   _____

g I took a umbrella with me because I thought it would rain.   _____

Antarctica

Read the passage.

Color the object the meteorologists sent into the atmosphere.

Highlight three things the balloon recorded.

Put a box around what the glaciologist was drilling.

Underline the reason glaciologists study ice cores.

Research stations in Antarctica are busy places. A visitor might describe a typical day like this:

Early this morning I joined a group of meteorologists as they launched a weather balloon. The balloon rose high into the sky and recorded temperature, wind speed, and air pressure. Scientists then studied the results.

After that, I watched a glaciologist drill ice cores. Ice cores contain air bubbles of gas from thousands of years ago. Glaciologists study the ice cores to learn more about the Earth's atmosphere.

Circle the correct answer for each question.

1 **What** did the meteorologists send into the atmosphere?
   a   a hot air balloon
   b   a helium balloon
   c   a weather balloon
   d   a water balloon

2 What word can **best replace** the phrase *temperature, wind speed, and air pressure*?
   a   tornadoes
   b   weather
   c   hurricanes
   d   snowstorms

3 Based on your answers to questions 1 and 2, what is the **best definition** of a meteorologist? Someone who studies how ...
   a   weather affects the environment.
   b   balloons affect the environment.
   c   tornadoes form.
   d   snowstorms form.

4 What is a *glacier*? A slowly moving mass of ...
   a   mud
   b   soil
   c   water
   d   ice

5 What does a *glaciologist* most likely study? All forms of ...
   a   soil
   b   ice
   c   water
   d   mud

L.4.4.A Use context (e.g., definitions, examples, or restatements in text) as a clue to the meaning of a word or phrase.

Antarctica

Read the full text

Antarctica

Read the passage.

Underline what the geologists were doing.

Color the information contained in the rock samples.

Research stations in Antarctica are busy places. A visitor might describe a typical afternoon like this:

After lunch, I flew by helicopter to where geologists were collecting rock samples. These contain important information about the Earth from millions of years ago.

Finally, I saw a marine biologist check the electronic tag that was glued to a Weddell seal. These tags record information about where marine animals travel in the ocean.

Highlight what the biologist was doing.

Circle the key word that helps us work out what the word *marine* means.

1 **What** were the geologists doing?

_____

_____

2 **What** information do the rocks contain?

_____

_____

3 Use your answers to questions 1 and 2 to help you write a description of **what** a geologist does.

_____

_____

_____

4 **What** is a *marine animal*?

_____

_____

L.4.4.A Use context (e.g., definitions, examples, or restatements in text) as a clue to the meaning of a word or phrase.

73

Digraphs: ie, ei

Two letters that make a single sound are called a **digraph**.
The letters **ie** usually make the single sound **ee**; e.g., field.
The letters **ei** sometimes make the single sound **ee**; e.g., s**ei**ze.
Always use **ei** when the **ee** sound comes **after c**; e.g., re**cei**ve.

List **1** **Write the word.**

chief _____
field _____
piece _____
priest _____
shield _____
ceiling _____
veil _____
their _____
brief _____
friend _____
fierce _____
patient _____
mischief _____
receive _____
deceit _____
grieve _____
shriek _____
heir _____
either _____
believe _____

2 **Sort the words.**

a ie

_____ _____
_____ _____
_____ _____
_____ _____
_____ _____
_____ _____

b ei

_____ _____
_____ _____
_____ _____
_____ _____

3 **Name.**

a _____ **b** _____

4 **Meaning.** Which list word means?

a Playful behavior that causes trouble _____

b The leader of a group _____

c To be able to wait without complaining _____

d A person who will receive another's property _____

e A piece of armor worn to protect _____

f A thin piece of cloth _____

Digraphs: ie, ei

1 **Revise your spelling list from page 74.** Underline the spelling mistakes. Write the word correctly.

a Our coach always seemed to beleive in our team. _____

b The lies and deciet ruined their friendship. _____

c She let out a skreik of excitement. _____

d The feild was full of poppies. _____

e The bride wore a viel that covered her face. _____

f Thier baseball game started at ten o'clock. _____

g My freind and I play basketball on the weekend. _____

h The warrior held up a huge sheild before running into battle. _____

Challenge words

2 **Write the word.**

protein _____

sieve _____

yield _____

siege _____

seize _____

leisure _____

weird _____

feisty _____

achieve _____

ancient _____

3 **Complete the sentence.**

a To _____ the color green I need blue and yellow paint.

b Eggs and meat are good sources of _____.

c The _____ of the castle only lasted two days before the king surrendered.

d Our bake sale did not _____ much profit.

4 **Another way to say it.** Which challenge word could replace the underlined words?

a I tried to <u>grab</u> the remote off my sister. _____

b His behavior is very <u>strange</u>. _____

c The little boy has a rather <u>aggressive</u> nature. _____

d During our <u>relaxation</u> time I went down to the beach. _____

Noun phrases

A **phrase** is a part of a sentence that has **more than one word**. A **noun phrase** is the group of words that is **built around a noun**. It can include:

- **determiners**; e.g., a, the, that, some, two, many, several
- **adjectives**; e.g., enormous, green, happy, wooden, Indian
- **other phrases**; e.g., of birds, with a long tail, in the front

1 **Complete these noun phrases with words from the box.**

some   of   on   seventh   an   at   from

a   the mess _____ the floor

b   musicians _____ the back

c   _____ pretty little flowers

d   _____ egg _____ the carton

e   _____ day _____ the week

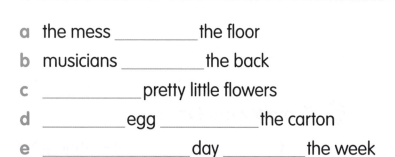

2 **Match the beginnings and endings.**

a   the giraffe calf   on the corner

b   some pears   around the collar

c   that large house   with the wobbly legs

d   several colorful birds   from our orchard

e   a fancy frill   in the jungle

3 **Circle the most important word in each underlined phrase.**

a   <u>All three balls in the bag</u> belong to me.

b   She is reading <u>a book by the famous author</u>.

c   <u>The little boy at the bus stop</u> is eating a plum.

d   Goldilocks fell asleep in <u>Baby Bear's comfortable bed</u>.

L.4.1 Demonstrate command of the conventions of standard English grammar and usage when writing or speaking.

Energy

Read the passage.

Color four things that can make electricity.

Circle the key word that tells how fuels such as coal can be turned into electricity.

Underline how sunlight is captured to make electricity.

Highlight what happens to water when it is heated.

Put a box around the verb that tells how steam powers a turbine.

The most common way to make electricity is to burn a fuel, such as coal. This heats water to make steam. The steam spins a turbine. This powers a generator to make electricity.

There are other ways to make electricity. Wind and water can also power a generator. A solar cell absorbs sunlight to make electricity.

Electrical energy can be converted into other forms of energy, such as heat, light, and sound.

Lightning is an electrical current that jumps through the air. The current heats the air hotter than the surface of the Sun.

Circle the correct answer/s for each question.

1 What is the **main idea** or **key point** of the passage?

a   why electricity is made

b   how electricity is made

c   where electricity is made

d   when electricity is made

2 Which three **details** best **support the main idea**?

a   Lightning is an electrical current that jumps through the air.

b   Electricity is made by burning coal.

c   A solar cell absorbs sunlight to make electricity.

d   Electrical energy can be converted into heat.

e   Wind and water can power a generator to make electricity.

Energy

Read the full text

Energy

Read the passage.

Underline what potential energy is.

Color what kinetic energy is.

Work waiting to be done is potential energy. Work being done is kinetic energy.

Potential energy is energy that could be released or used. A coiled spring has potential energy because the spring could uncoil. A rock on the edge of a cliff has potential energy. Its potential energy is the energy that would be released if it fell from the cliff.

The food we eat becomes potential energy when it is stored in our bodies. When this energy is used to do things, such as kick a ball, it becomes kinetic energy.

Circle an example of potential energy.

Put a box around an example of kinetic energy.

1 What is the passage **mainly** about? _____

_____

2 List three **details** that **support the main idea**.

a _____

_____

_____

b _____

_____

_____

c _____

_____

RI.4.2 Determine the main idea of a text and explain how it is supported by key details; summarize the text.

Suffix: ly

Adding the suffix **ly** to an adjective turns it into an adverb; e.g., first → first**ly**.

If the adjective ends in **y**, change the **y** to **i** before adding **ly**; e.g., bus**y** → bus**ily**.

List ① Write the word.

briskly _____

rarely _____

firmly _____

gently _____

truly _____

firstly _____

secondly _____

sharply _____

finally _____

honestly _____

rapidly _____

publicly _____

slightly _____

normally _____

similarly _____

personally _____

roughly _____

instantly _____

terribly _____

promptly _____

② Word building. Add the suffix ly to build the words.

obvious _obviously_

a final _____

b gentle _____

c honest _____

d prompt _____

e sharp _____

f personal _____

g first _____

③ Unscramble these list words.

a nhylsoet _____

b dcselnyo _____

c rpyaild _____

d rtyeribl _____

e onperslaly _____

f skribyl _____

g negtly _____

h nlalyfi _____

④ Missing letter. Fill in the missing letters.

a bri_____

b tr_____

c in_____

d ro_____

e no_____

f sli_____

g sh_____

⑤ Chunks. Rearrange to make a list word.

a son ly per al _____

b lic pub ly _____

c est hon ly _____

d dly con se _____

e mal nor ly _____

f il ly ar sim _____

g pt prom ly _____

Suffix: ly

1 **Revise your spelling list from page 79.** Fill in the missing words.

a After walking b_____ for several minutes we f_____ arrived at our destination.

b There are many reasons to recycle; f_____ , it reduces waste, and s_____ , it is good for the environment.

c I can h_____ say that I am very nervous about speaking p_____ .

d My mother was t_____ shocked at how r_____ I did all my chores.

e N_____ I arrive at soccer practice p_____ at 8 o'clock.

Challenge words

2 **Write the word.**

actually _____

obviously _____

eventually _____

generally _____

apparently _____

necessarily _____

gradually _____

desperately _____

vaguely _____

conveniently _____

3 **Hidden words.** Find the challenge words.

a gdseventuallyxfd _____

b dvdnecessarilysd _____

c dfdsvaguelysdges _____

d dfsplapparentlys _____

e sdfsobviouslysdf _____

f dgvdractuallygvsre _____

g hbgfuigraduallyo _____

h jkpodesperatelyk _____

i entconvenientlyvi _____

j llygenerallygenell _____

4 **Another way to say it.** Which challenge word could replace the underlined words?

a Why did you make a joke when he is <u>clearly</u> upset? _____

b After a long hike we <u>finally</u> made it to the top. _____

c I <u>usually</u> have cereal for breakfast. _____

d I am <u>slowly</u> getting better at math. _____

e After the game, I was <u>urgently</u> in need of a drink of water. _____

Prepositions

A **preposition** shows the relationship between a noun or pronoun and other words in a sentence. It often introduces a phrase that tells **where**, **when**, **why**, or **how** something happens; e.g., Harry practices **in** the afternoon. They paint **for** fun. She arrived **on** horseback.

A phrase that starts with a preposition can also give us information about a noun; e.g., I live in the house **with** the red roof.

1 **Complete the following sentences with prepositions from the box.**

in	about	over	into	beside	to	of	with	by
	through	along	on	across	at			

a   I went _____ the beach _____ my friends.

b   A flock _____ birds flew _____ our house.

c   My friend lives _____ the house _____ the corner.

d   The book _____ Roald Dahl is _____ a boy called Charlie.

e   She looked _____ the stars _____ a large telescope.

f   I dived _____ the water and swam _____ the pool.

g   I walked _____ the path that ran _____ the river.

2 **Circle the preposition in parentheses that correctly completes each sentence.**

a   The new boy comes (for, from) Europe.

b   The coin rolled (under, among) my bed.

c   We found the cause (of, off) the problem.

d   If you freeze water it will turn (in, into) ice.

e   They raced each other (with, down) the stairs.

f   The child was hiding (between, behind) the tree.

3 **Circle three prepositions in this poem by Robert Louis Stevenson.**

Where Go the Boats?
Dark brown is the river,
Golden is the sand.
It flows along for ever,
With trees on either hand.

Green leaves a-floating,
Castles of the foam,
Boats of mine a-boating-
Where will all come home?

The Arctic

Read the passage.

Underline why many countries argue over who owns the Arctic.

Color the reason Russian scientists researched the land beneath the Arctic Ocean.

Highlight how much oil and natural gas there is in the Arctic.

If you don't know what the term *oil and gas deposits* means, put a **W** next to it. If you know what the term means, put a ✔ next to it.

The countries that make up the Arctic often argue about who owns it. Many countries want the Arctic's valuable oil and gas deposits.

In 2007, 50 Russian scientists used a mini submarine to research the seabed under the North Pole. They were trying to prove that the land underneath the Arctic Ocean is connected to their land in Siberia. They even planted a Russian flag on the seabed.

There are over 10 billion tons of oil and natural gas deposits in the Arctic territory. Canada, Norway, and Greenland are also trying to prove that they own the land under the Arctic waters.

Circle the correct answer for each question.

1 What is the author's **main purpose** in writing this text?

a to persuade readers that Russia owns the land beneath the Arctic waters

b to inform readers about the countries that are trying to prove ownership of the Arctic

c to entertain readers with stories about the Arctic

2 Who is the **target audience** for this text?

a scientists

b politicians

c oil and gas companies

d the general public

3 What is the **clue** to question 2's answer? The author uses language that ...

a most people can understand.

b only scientists can understand.

c only politicians can understand.

d only adults can understand.

The Arctic

Read the full text

The Arctic

Read the passage.

Underline the definition of an igloo.

Color what size the blocks of snow should be.

Circle all the verbs that give orders.

An igloo is a dome-shaped shelter, made out of blocks of snow.

What you need:

• A snow saw   • Dry snow

What to do:

1. Use the saw to cut blocks of hard, dry snow, about one yard long and 40 inches deep.

2. Draw a circle in the snow and stand in the middle of it. Place the blocks around the circle in layers. The blocks of snow should overlap and lean towards the center.

3. Place the last block on top of the igloo. Cut it to fit the hole.

4. Cut a tunnel under the wall for the entrance. Poke small breathing holes in the walls.

Highlight the instruction that tells how to form the blocks of snow into a dome shape.

Put a box around the key word that tells how people will enter and leave the igloo.

1 What is the **purpose** of the text?

_____

2 List six **verbs** that **helped you work out the answer** to question 1.

_____

3 **Who** would be most likely to build an igloo?

_____

4 Do you **think** that people who live in places where it doesn't snow would be interested in reading the text? Give one or more reasons for your answer.

_____

_____

5 Based on your answer to question 4, who is the **target audience** for the text?

_____

Homophones

> **Homophones** are words that sound the same but are spelled differently and have different meanings; e.g., where, wear.

List

ball

bawl

foul

fowl

yoke

yolk

tide

tied

maze

maize

throne

thrown

lessen

lesson

seen

scene

fort

fought

threw

through

① Write the word.

_____

_____

_____

_____

_____

_____

_____

_____

_____

_____

_____

_____

_____

_____

_____

_____

_____

_____

_____

_____

② Name.

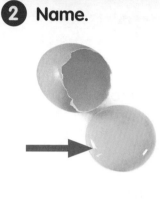

a _____   b _____

c _____   d _____

③ Fill in the missing letters.

a l ___ s ___ o ___   b th ___ o ___ g ___

c f ___ ___ gh ___   d sc ___ n ___

e t ___ r ___ n ___   f f ___ w ___

g t ___ d ___   h m ___ i ___ e

④ Meaning. Which list word means?

a A wooden bar that joins two work animals

b Corn

c To wail or cry loudly

d Paths between high walls meant to confuse

e Birds such as chickens, turkeys, geese, and ducks

f To make something smaller

g A strong building used during battles

_____

_____

_____

_____

_____

_____

_____

L.4.2.D Spell grade-appropriate words correctly.

Homophones

1 **Revise your spelling list from page 84.** Which homophone goes where?

a The clucking _____ smelled quite _____. (foul, fowl)

b They _____ over the best spot to build the _____. (fort, fought)

c The tall _____ plants formed a _____. (maize, maze)

d The boys _____ the ball _____ the hoop. (through, threw)

e The queen had _____ her crown onto her _____. (throne, thrown)

f They _____ up the boat at high _____. (tide, tied)

g The baby likes to _____ if he doesn't get his _____. (ball, bawl)

Challenge words

2 **Write the word.**

crews _____
cruise _____
weather _____
whether _____
effect _____
affect _____
guest _____
guessed _____
accept _____
except _____

3 **Word clues.** Which challenge word means?

a sun, rain, wind, snow _____

b a trip on a ship _____

c a visitor _____

d to receive something _____

e not including _____

f workers in teams _____

g to influence _____

h a result _____

4 **Complete the sentence.**

a My grandparents are going on a _____ to the Caribbean.

b I wasn't sure _____ to wear my new dress or pants.

c His mood had an _____ on all his friends.

d I _____ the correct number of beans in the jar.

e The _____ report predicted sunny skies all weekend.

f Your hard work will _____ your baseball skills.

Prepositional phrases

A **phrase** is a part of a sentence that is more than one word. Many phrases that **do the work of an adjective or adverb** start with a preposition; e.g., The young girl **with** **the bow** (gives information about the girl) is sitting **on** **the bench** (tells where she is sitting).

1 **Complete each phrase with a preposition from the box.**

of   in   with   on   from   to

a   A cat always lands _____ its feet.

b   Their visitors arrived _____ three o'clock.

c   Some people _____ the crowd were very noisy.

d   Our new neighbor comes _____ South America.

e   The kittens are playing _____ the ball _____ wool.

2 **Which word in parentheses correctly completes each sentence?**

a   My father travels to work (on, by) _____ bus.

b   The animal (with, at) _____ the stumpy tail is a bear.

c   My friend lives (on, in) _____ the house (on, in) _____ the corner.

d   Lots (off, of) _____ people get their water (for, from) _____ the lake.

e   I gave the book (to, for) _____ my friend to read.

f   My cousins live (near, from) _____ the beach.

g   They are building a wall (around, since) _____ the vegetable garden.

3 **Check (✔) the phrases that can correctly complete the following sentence.**

The child is playing _____.

a   ☐ in the garden   b   ☐ with the dog   c   ☐ from the house

d   ☐ on the grass   e   ☐ beside the pond   f   ☐ by train

g   ☐ through the window   h   ☐ near the flower bed   i   ☐ from the beach

L.4.1.E Form and use prepositional phrases.

Advertisements

Read the passage.

(Circle) the words that helped you see what kind of service the advertiser offers.

Highlight the words that helped you see what the advertiser's quotes are based on.

Underline the words that helped you see what other jobs the advertiser does.

It's summer—let us mow your lawn! Our fast, on time lawn mowing service always does a great job. Long list of happy customers, who enjoy professional work with a smile. Free quotes based on the size of your lawn, how many trees in it, and how overgrown it is for the first mow. We also do yard cleanups, weed removal, and gutter clearing. No job too big or small.

1. Read the passage again. As you do, visualize what you are reading about. Draw a picture of the images you create.

The kind of service the advertiser offers	Other jobs the advertiser does

What the advertiser's quotes are based on

RI.4.1 Refer to details and examples in a text when explaining what the text says explicitly and when drawing inferences from the text.

87

Advertisements

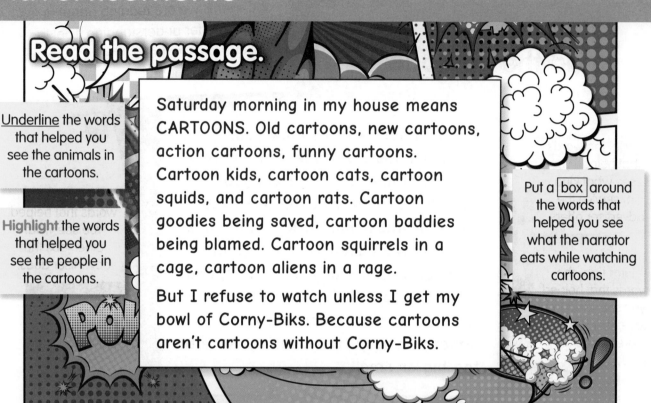

Read the passage.

Underline the words that helped you see the animals in the cartoons.

Highlight the words that helped you see the people in the cartoons.

Saturday morning in my house means CARTOONS. Old cartoons, new cartoons, action cartoons, funny cartoons. Cartoon kids, cartoon cats, cartoon squids, and cartoon rats. Cartoon goodies being saved, cartoon baddies being blamed. Cartoon squirrels in a cage, cartoon aliens in a rage.

But I refuse to watch unless I get my bowl of Corny-Biks. Because cartoons aren't cartoons without Corny-Biks.

Put a box around the words that helped you see what the narrator eats while watching cartoons.

1 Read the passage again. As you do, visualize what you are reading about. Draw a picture of the images you create.

Cartoon animals

Cartoon people

Narrator eating breakfast

RI.4.1 Refer to details and examples in a text when explaining what the text says explicitly and when drawing inferences from the text.

Endings: ent, ant

Many words that end in **ent** and **ant** have the same end sound; e.g., confid**ent**, pleas**ant**.

List

1 Write the word.

present _____

distant _____

servant _____

parent _____

silent _____

infant _____

talent _____

recent _____

absent _____

student _____

vacant _____

important _____

merchant _____

continent _____

frequent _____

pleasant _____

elephant _____

dependent _____

confident _____

contestant _____

2 Sort the words.

a ent

_____ _____

_____ _____

_____ _____

_____ _____

_____ _____

b ant

_____ _____

_____ _____

_____ _____

_____ _____

_____ _____

3 In a group. Write the list word that belongs in each group.

a quiet, mute, _____

b empty, unoccupied, _____

c main, significant, _____

d land, country, _____

e scholar, pupil, _____

4 Name.

a _____   b _____   c _____   d _____

Endings: ent, ant

1 **Revise your spelling list from page 89.** Which list word means?

a   far away

_____

b   not present

_____

c   a natural ability or skill

_____

d   a person who buys and sells goods

_____

e   large animal with a trunk

_____

f   one of seven land masses

_____

Challenge words

2 **Write the word.**

different   _____

arrogant   _____

innocent   _____

fragrant   _____

hesitant   _____

permanent   _____

president   _____

assistant   _____

brilliant   _____

ignorant   _____

3 **Word clues.** Which challenge word means?

a   someone who helps

_____

b   not sure, in doubt   _____

c   not the same or alike

_____

d   acting more important than other people

_____

e   the title of some leaders

_____

f   not aware or informed

_____

4 **Complete the sentence.**

a   The _____ flowers filled the room with their sweet scent.

b   I was _____ to try out for the team, but my friends convinced me.

c   My grandpa is _____ about computers and how to use them.

d   Although she was blamed, I knew that she was _____.

e   My sister and I have two very _____ fashion styles.

f   Too much fame had given him an _____ attitude.

g   The sun can cause _____ skin damage.

L.4.2.D Spell grade-appropriate words correctly.

Fronted adverbials

A **fronted adverbial** is an **adverb** or an **adverbial phrase** that comes at the beginning of a sentence. It is always followed by a comma (,); e.g., **Carefully**, he placed the eggs on the table. **After lunch**, we went to see Grandpa.

1 **In the following sentences, fill in the commas.**

a After a while the children started to get bored.

b Silently the tiger stalked its prey.

c Without a word he left the room.

d Behind the clouds the sun is still shining.

e Quickly the ballerinas took their places.

f In a few minutes the storm will be over.

2 **Write each sentence so that the adverbial is at the front. Use the correct punctuation.**

a She ran to help the little boy without any hesitation. _____

_____

b He had finished his breakfast by 7 o'clock. _____

_____

c She crossed the road with a spring in her step. _____

_____

d We will know the results in a little while. _____

_____

e There are lots of shady trees beside the river. _____

_____

3 **Complete the following sentences. Use the correct punctuation.**

a Outside my house _____

_____

b In the middle of the night _____

_____

Simple Machines

Important information
To find the most important information in a text, look for the words, phrases, or sentences that tell us the most about the subject.

Read the passage.

Circle three verbs that tell what screws do.

Put a box around the tool that turns a screw.

Underline the sentence that gives the best description of a screw.

Color what the first screw machine was used for.

Screws hold things together, and lower and raise things.

A screw is an inclined plane wrapped around a cylinder. The inclined plane forms a ridge along the cylinder. This ridge is called the thread of the screw.

As a screw is turned by a screwdriver, it turns a greater distance than it moves forward. The turning motion becomes a forward motion.

A Greek mathematician called Archimedes invented a screw machine more than 2,200 years ago. It was used to lift water into fields and out of ships.

1 Which **three** sentences tell how a screw works? Circle the correct answers.

a Screws hold things together, and lower and raise things.

b A screw is an inclined plane wrapped around a cylinder.

c The inclined plane forms a ridge along the cylinder.

d This ridge is called the thread of the screw.

e As a screw is turned by a screwdriver, it turns a greater distance than it moves forward.

f Some screws work by lowering and raising things.

g A Greek mathematician called Archimedes invented a screw machine more than 2,200 years ago.

2 Of the three sentences you chose in question 1, write out the one you think best sums up what screws are used for.

_____

_____

RI.4.1 Refer to details and examples in a text when explaining what the text says explicitly and when drawing inferences from the text.

Simple Machines

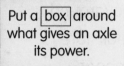

Read the
full text

Simple
Machines

Read the passage.

Circle two verbs that tell what a wheel fitted with an axle does.

Highlight the example of a wheel and axle.

A wheel with a rod, called an axle, through its center can lift and move loads.

The axle is joined to the wheel. When either the wheel or axle turns, the other part also turns. The steering wheel in a car is a wheel and axle.

The circle turned by a wheel is much larger than the circle turned by the axle. The longer distance turned by the wheel makes the axle turn more powerfully.

A wheel and axle is often used with gears. A gear is a wheel with cogs around its edge. Several gears can be connected, so that their cogs lock into each other.

Put a box around what gives an axle its power.

Color the sentence that explains what a gear is.

1 Write out the sentence that **best describes** what a wheel fitted with an axle can do.

_____

_____

2 Find and write out the sentence that **explains how** a wheel and axle work together.

_____

_____

3 Find and write out two sentences that give **examples** of ways a wheel and axle can be used.

_____

_____

_____

RI.4.1 Refer to details and examples in a text when explaining what the text says explicitly and when drawing inferences from the text.

93

Compound words

> **Compound words** are two or more words that make one word; e.g., grapefruit, breakfast.

List **1** **Write the word.**

necklace _____

sometimes _____

playground _____

bookstore _____

lifeboat _____

seashore _____

underground _____

horseback _____

handcuff _____

backstage _____

staircase _____

fingerprint _____

password _____

dishwasher _____

sunbathe _____

forehead _____

suitcase _____

footstep _____

dragonfly _____

meanwhile _____

2 **Name.**

a _____   b _____

c _____   d _____

3 **Missing letters.** Write the missing letters.

a _____case   b _____fly

c some_____   d _____shore

e _____word   f under_____

g _____head   h hand_____

4 **Word clues.** Which list word matches?

a everyone has an individual one _____

b a place to buy reading material _____

c worn around the neck _____

d where you find swings _____

e something to pack your clothes in _____

f a secret word _____

g where moles live _____

h a machine for dirty dishes _____

L.4.2.D Spell grade-appropriate words correctly.

Compound words

1 Revise your spelling list from page 94.
Rearrange to make a list word.

a ba the sun _____

b he ad fo re _____

c ep fo st ot _____

d an wh me ile _____

e me ti mes so _____

2 Unscramble these list words.

a sofoptet _____

b ershwashdi _____

c gerinfintpr _____

d baagestck _____

e oserhacbk _____

f ooookbster _____

Challenge words

3 Write the word.

toothpaste _____

keyboard _____

flashlight _____

hairdresser _____

saucepan _____

weatherman _____

earthworm _____

peppermint _____

firefighter _____

granddaughter _____

4 Hidden words. Find the challenge word.

a ugtgranddaughter _____

b intpeppermintpe _____

c boarkeyboardkey _____

d figetfirefighterferi _____

e serhairdresserieir _____

f skdpasaucepansk _____

g saweathermansfs _____

h lsapstoothpastesd _____

i sdflashlightsdse _____

j wormearthworme _____

5 Complete the sentence.

a When the lights went out I hurried to find a _____.

b While digging in the garden I came across a large _____.

c I squeezed the rest of the _____ onto my toothbrush.

d A _____ has a large, strong jaw to munch through mulberry leaves.

e I cooked pasta for dinner in the large _____.

f The _____ quickly put out the blaze.

g My favorite ice cream flavor is _____.

Possessive nouns

Apostrophes (') show:
- where letters have been left out when words are joined together (contractions); e.g., didn't (did not) we're (we are).
- possession; e.g., the dog's bone.

1 **Sort the phrases.**

that's mine   baby's bottle   isn't yours   donkey's ears   boy's bike   I'm six

I've finished   bird's nest   you'll need   we're leaving   cyclist's helmet

Contractions	Possessive nouns

2 **Complete each sentence with a word from the box.**

a He won't be at his _____ house until later.

b My _____ bowl isn't in his kennel.

c I think he's riding his _____ new bike.

d The _____ car doesn't fit in the garage.

dog's

man's

sister's

friend's

3 **Complete each sentence by forming the possessive noun.**

a "Look at the (pig) _____ curly tail," shouted Sarah.

b "But where's your (sister) _____ hat?" asked Dad.

c (Henry) _____ favorite books are all about dinosaurs.

d I gave the ice cream to the (boy) _____ brother.

L.4.2 Demonstrate command of the conventions of standard English capitalization, punctuation, and spelling when writing.

Spelling

Use this review to test your knowledge. It has three parts—**Spelling, Grammar,** and **Comprehension**. If you're unsure of an answer, go back and read the rules and generalizations in the blue boxes.

You have learned about:

- prefixes: un, dis, mis
- suffixes: er, est
- homophones
- plurals
- digraphs: ie and ei
- endings: ent, ant
- endings: ice, ise, ize
- suffix: ly
- compound words

1 **In each sentence, an error has been <u>underlined</u>. Write the correct word.** 2 marks

  a   You're the <u>braver</u> girl I know.   _____

  b   "What is that <u>fowl</u> smell?" cried the coach.   _____

  c   On my new bike I could ride <u>fastest</u> than my sister.   _____

  d   Even though I'm the youngest brother, I'm not the <u>shorter</u>.   _____

2 **Which word correctly completes this sentence?** 1 mark

Grandma's diaries helped her quickly recall _____ from when she was young.

  a   memorys   b   memory's   c   memories   d   memory

3 **Which word correctly completes this sentence?** 1 mark

The _____ spy was charged with treason.

  a   unloyal   b   disloyal   c   misloyal   d   loyally

4 **Write the sounds ie or ei to correctly complete these words.** 2 marks

  a   rec __ __ ve   b   th __ __ r   c   misch __ __ f   d   p __ __ ce

5 **This sentence has one word that is incorrect. Write the correct word.** 1 mark

I personal believe that we should read more books.   _____

6 **Write the sounds ice, ise, or ize to correctly complete these words.** 2 marks

  a   prom __ __ __   b   organ __ __ __   c   prejud __ __ __   d   surpr __ __ __

7 **Write the compound word.** 1 mark

  a   + = _____

  b   + = _____

Your score

[ ]

10

Grammar

You have learned about:

- adjectives
- noun phrases
- fronted adverbials

- adverbs
- prepositions
- possessive nouns

- determiners
- prepositional phrases

....

1 **Rewrite the following sentences so that the adjectives are in the correct order.** 2 marks

   a My friend has a white Persian fluffy kitten.

_____

   b We spotted large African three elephants in the distance.

_____

2 **Write down whether the underlined adverbs show how, where, or when.** 2 marks

   a The children crossed the road <u>quickly</u>.   _____

   b The sun will go down <u>soon</u>.   _____

   c I looked <u>up</u> when I heard the plane.   _____

   d She packed away her clothes <u>neatly</u>.   _____

3 **Circle the word in parentheses that correctly completes each sentence.** Write down whether the word is an adjective or an adverb. 3 marks

   a He was (careful, carefully) not to spill the milk.   _____

   b (Careful, Carefully), he poured the milk into the glass.   _____

   c My horse should (easy, easily) clear that fence.   _____

4 **Circle the word in parentheses that correctly completes each sentence.** 2 marks

   a The children found (a, an) egg in the nest.

   b Put (that, those) books on the shelf.

   c Have you read (this, these) book?

   d Each dog has (it's, its) own kennel.

5 **In each sentence, underline the longest noun phrase.** 1 mark

   a The players watched as a flock of birds flew by.

   b The children are sitting on the stone bench beneath the old oak tree.

Grammar

6 **Complete each sentence with a preposition from the box.** Use each word once. 3 marks

for	around	beside	under	about	through

a I sat _____ my mother on the bus.

b A fly was buzzing _____ my head.

c I made the card _____ my best friend.

d My cat likes to hide _____ my bed.

e I like to read stories _____ heroes and villains.

f The train has to go _____ a tunnel.

7 **In each sentence, underline the prepositional phrase.** 2 marks

a Jaguars hunt at dawn and dusk.　　b Jaguars hunt fish with their paws.

c Jaguars live in thick, tropical jungles.　　d Jaguars have dark spots on their coats.

8 **Rewrite the following sentences so that they start with the underlined word or phrase.** 3 marks

a My alarm wakes me up <u>at 6 o'clock every morning</u>.

_____

b I could see a herd of elephants <u>in the distance</u>.

_____

c The children removed the weeds <u>carefully</u>.

_____

9 **In the following sentences, fill in the missing apostrophes.** 2 marks

a I think the cats toy is under one of those chairs.

b The ducklings followed their mother to the waters edge.

Your
score

[   ]

20

The Time Keepers

Read the passage and then use the comprehension skills you have learned to answer the questions.

Clocks have been ticking away the time for centuries. The oldest clock in existence today is in a cathedral in England. It is over 700 years old.

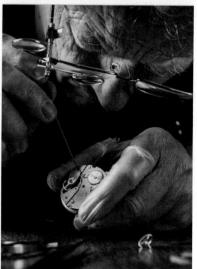

Many early clocks had no hands and no faces. They told time simply by striking the hour. Bells were an important part of these clocks. In fact, the word clock comes from the French word, *cloche*, meaning 'bell.'

Early clocks relied on a falling weight to turn wheels inside the clock to tick away the time. They were not good time keepers. They could lose or gain half an hour to two hours a day.

The first hand to be introduced was the hour hand. Often it did not move. Instead, the numbers marked on the face of the clock moved. The minute hand was introduced when a pendulum replaced the falling weight and after that, time keeping became more reliable. Later, a spring replaced the pendulum in many clocks. A key was used to wind the spring inside the case and it would slowly unwind to tick away the time. A second key wound a spring that struck a bell every hour. Time keeping became much more accurate.

The first watches appeared about 500 years ago. Some early watches struck the hours, but most had to be watched—hence the name, watch.

Once, all clocks and watches were handmade. Nowadays, many are made by machines in factories. There are all sorts of watches—pocket watches, wrist watches, digital watches, and stop watches. There are all sorts of wall, mantel, and desk clocks. There are digital clocks, clocks with alarms, cuckoo clocks, electric clocks, and grandfather clocks.

1 Where is the world's oldest existing clock? 1 mark   LITERAL

   a in a castle in England   **b** in a cathedral in England
   c in a museum in England   **d** in a country house in England

The Time Keepers

2 How were early clocks different from later ones? Later clocks ... 1 mark **INFERENTIAL**

   a had no faces or hands.   b were made of wood.

   c were accurate time keepers.   d were made in factories.

3 Give a text clue to support your answer to question 2. 2 marks **CRITICAL**

_____

_____

4 Why is it helpful for people to know the time? Choose the best answer. 1 mark **CRITICAL**

Knowing the time helps people ...

   a relax.   b sleep at night.

   c organize their lives.   d lead healthier lives.

5 What is a pendulum? 1 mark **VOCABULARY**

   a a pointer   b a type of key

   c a swinging weight   d a type of watch

6 In the text, what is a spring? 1 mark **VOCABULARY**

   a a sudden movement   b a coil of wire

   c a change in the weather   d a type of well

7 In what way are all clocks and watches similar? They all ... 1 mark **INFERENTIAL**

   a have minute and hour hands.   b make sounds.

   c tell the time.   d look the same.

8 How did the watch get its name? 2 marks **LITERAL**

_____

Your score

☐

10

_____

_____

Your Review 2 Scores

Spelling		Grammar		Comprehension		Total
☐	+	☐	+	☐	=	☐
10		**20**		**10**		**40**

Kevin's Echidna

Figurative language

Similes and metaphors use comparisons to help you visualize pictures. Similes compare one thing to something else using the words *like* or *as*. Metaphors make a more direct comparison. They do not use *like* or *as*.

Read the passage.

Highlight the objects the echidna's quills are compared to.

Color the objects the hairs on the echidna's face are compared to.

Kevin could see the echidna so clearly—its black-tipped, creamy quills, as sharp as knitting needles; the coarse, black hairs on its face, like bristles on a brush; its eyes two beads shining against the dull blackness of its snout.

Put a box around the objects the echidna's eyes are compared to.

Circle the correct answer/s for each question.

1 Which **two** figures of speech are **similes**?
- a the coarse, black hair of its face, like bristles on a brush
- b the dull blackness of its snout
- c its eyes two beads
- d quills as sharp as knitting needles

2 Which **two** words helped you identify the **similes**?
- a as
- b on
- c against
- d like

3 What picture of the hairs on the echidna's face does the **simile** give us? The hairs on the echidna's face are …
- a long.
- b beautiful.
- c prickly.
- d colorful.

4 Which figure of speech is a **metaphor**?
- a like bristles on a brush
- b sharp as knitting needles
- c the dull blackness of its snout
- d its eyes two beads

5 What picture of the echidna's eyes does the **metaphor** give us? The echidna's eyes are …
- a small and bright.
- b big and dull.
- c oval and gray.
- d round and watery.

L.4.5 Demonstrate understanding of figurative language, word relationships, and nuances in word meanings.

Kevin's Echidna

Read the whole story

Read the passage.

Circle the object Kevin's legs are compared to.

Highlight the objects the leaves are compared to.

Kevin climbed to the highest branch of the tree and balanced there. His legs had turned to stone, but he forced himself to look down. Brown leaves were floating on the murky water, like little boats. He took a deep breath and plunged into the pool. It wasn't the greatest dive he had ever done, but as he surfaced, the fear was gone.

1 The writer **says** Kevin's legs had turned to stone. What **figure of speech** is this?

_____

2 What do you **think** the writer is telling us when he compares Kevin's legs to stone?

_____

3 Do you **think** this is a good way to describe how Kevin was feeling? Why, or why not?

_____

_____

4 The writer **compares** the brown leaves to little boats. What **figure of speech** is this?

_____

5 Do you **think** this is a good way of describing the leaves? Why, or why not?

_____

_____

_____

Past tense

> **Irregular verbs** do not have the suffix **ed** in the past tense. Some irregular verbs change their spelling and sound different in the past tense; e.g., blow → blew, catch → caught.
>
> Some irregular verbs do not change their spelling or sound different in the past tense; e.g., quit.

List

1 **Write the word.**

said _____

wept _____

paid _____

flew _____

flown _____

hurt _____

stuck _____

swung _____

beaten _____

drove _____

strode _____

written _____

slunk _____

swore _____

driven _____

forgiven _____

sprang _____

ridden _____

strung _____

brought _____

2 **Complete the table.**

say	said
stick	
write	
ride	
drive	
pay	
hurt	
string	

3 **Unscramble these list words.**

a gsuwn _____

b lknsu _____

c oredst _____

d ckuts _____

e unrtgs _____

f adpi _____

g lofnw _____

h angpsr _____

4 **Missing letter.** Fill in the missing letters.

a __ ep __

b ri __ __ __ n

c __ __ id

d f __ e __

e hu __ __

f __ ro __ e

g __ __ ung

h w __ it __ __ __

i __ __ __ ode

j __ __ unk

k sw __ __ __

l s __ __ d

5 **Chunks.** Rearrange the chunks to make a list word.

a tt wri en _____

b dd ri en _____

c ng ru st _____

d at be en _____

e giv for en _____

L.4.2.D Spell grade-appropriate words correctly.

Past tense

1 **Revise your spelling list from page 104.** Underline the mistakes.
Write the word correctly.

a The eagle fly high above the trees. _____

b He has write a lovely poem. _____

c The family has fly around the world. _____

d Mom pay the delivery man for the food. _____

e Dad has drive them to practice. _____

f Genna say that she would be home on time. _____

g She hasn't ride a horse in months. _____

Challenge words

2 **Write the word.**

beheld _____

foresaw _____

overheard _____

underwent _____

foretold _____

interwoven _____

taught _____

understood _____

outgrown _____

withdrew _____

3 **Word clues.** Which challenge word means?

a predicted _____

b gave lessons _____

c twisted together _____

d became too big _____

e took away _____

f eavesdropped _____

g known _____

h saw what could happen

_____

4 **Complete the sentence.**

a I accidentally _____ them talking in the garage yesterday.

b I _____ the story after she explained it.

c I have green thread _____ into my blue sweater.

d He has _____ yet another pair of shoes.

e Yesterday we were _____ how to do simple multiplication.

Punctuating dialogue

> **Direct speech** repeats the actual words a speaker says.
> - Quotation marks (" ") are used around the actual words someone says, including any punctuation.
> - The first word a speaker says always starts with a capital letter; e.g.,
>   Zoe said, "That is my bag."
>   "That is my bag," said Zoe, "and this is yours."   BUT
>   "That is my bag," said Zoe. "Where is yours?"

1 **In the following sentences, circle the words that need capital letters.**

a simon said, "my cat has a soft coat and a long tail."

b "whose ball is this?" asked our coach. "is it yours?"

c "put some water in the kettle," she said, "and switch it on."

d zack said, "have you ever been on a big cruise ship? my cousin has."

e "the milk is in the fridge," he said, "and the cookies are in the cupboard."

f "you can't surf today," said the lifeguard. "the waves are too dangerous."

g "the chimpanzees were funny," said the child, "but I also liked the penguins."

2 **Check (✔) the sentences that have the correct punctuation.**

a Grandpa said, "I have lost my keys. Do you know where they are?" ☐

b Grandma said, "your keys are on the counter next to the stove." ☐

c "Why are you crying?" asked the lady. "have you hurt yourself?" ☐

d "I fell off the swing," said Oscar, "and scraped my knee and elbow." ☐

e "I'm wearing new shoes," said Sasha, "And they're pinching my toes." ☐

f "I don't like muffins," said Andy, "but I love pancakes." ☐

3 **Complete the following sentence. Use the correct punctuation.**

"The soup is very hot," said Mom, "so _____

_____

L.4.2 Demonstrate command of the conventions of standard English punctuation when writing.

Buzz, the Computer Man

To interpret a character's feelings and why they act in a certain way, look for clues in the text. The clues are usually in the words and punctuation.

Read the passage.

Put a box around the narrator's name.

Underline what Samantha said to Lisa.

Circle the punctuation that helps to show that Samantha was angry.

Color how Samantha planned to get back at Lisa.

"If I win the map-a-thon," said Lisa, "I don't want to take Samantha to Wonderland. I want to take Sarah." Sarah is her best friend.

I couldn't believe that Lisa wouldn't want to take me. She knew how much I wanted to go to Wonderland. I didn't keep it a secret.

"You're the meanest person I know!" I told her. "It would serve you right if someone else won the tickets to Wonderland."

I decided I would do my best to try to win. Then I'd take one of my friends instead of Lisa.

I grabbed her atlas and went to my bedroom to study.

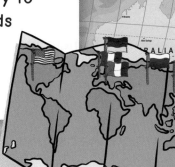

Circle the correct answer for each question.

1 How did Samantha **feel** when Lisa said she wanted to take Sarah to Wonderland?
   a pleased   b confused   c upset   d excited

2 What is a **clue** to question 1's answer? Samantha accused Lisa of being ...
   a a liar.   b lazy.   c a cheat.   d mean.

3 Which **punctuation** helps to answer question 1?
   a .   b ,   c !   d "

4 Why did Samantha decide to study for the map-a-thon? She wanted to ...
   a win the map-a-thon.   b take Lisa to Wonderland.
   c help Lisa win.   d show Lisa how clever she was.

RL.4.3 Describe in depth a character, setting, or event in a story or drama, drawing on specific details in the text.   **107**

Buzz, the Computer Man

Read the
whole story

Read the passage.

Highlight the words that show that the narrator was scared of Ram.

Ⓒircle two words that show that Ram was angry.

When Ram saw me, he stopped shouting. I hid behind Buzz, trying to make myself as small as possible.

Ram frowned. He loomed over Buzz. "Do you know the penalty for bringing an outsider into the computer?" he roared.

Buzz nodded. "But I was hoping you would see this as a special case," Buzz said, "and show a little kindness to a poor girl who needs the help of your great wisdom."

Ram stopped frowning and began to smile a little.

Buzz told Ram about the map-a-thon and the trouble that I'd been having. I needed something to help me remember the names of countries, and cities, and especially of oceans and seas.

Underline the words that Buzz used to praise Ram.

Put a box around what Ram did after Buzz praised him.

1 **Why** might the narrator have tried to make herself as small as possible?

_____

_____

2 **Which words** suggest that Ram was angry with Buzz?

_____

3 Carefully **explain how** Buzz made Ram smile.

_____

_____

4 Do you **think** that Ram will help the narrator? Give a reason for your answer.

_____

_____

_____

RL.4.3 Describe in depth a character, setting, or event in a story or drama, drawing on specific details in the text.

Endings: or, ure

The letters **or** and **ure** at the end of a word often make the sound **er**; e.g., rum**or** and treas**ure**.

List **①** **Write the word.**

color _____

nature _____

harbor _____

injure _____

rumor _____

labor _____

picture _____

mixture _____

favor _____

capture _____

odor _____

fracture _____

scripture _____

humor _____

adventure _____

treasure _____

janitor _____

honor _____

puncture _____

structure _____

② **Sort the words.**

a or _____ _____

_____ _____

_____ _____

_____ _____

_____ _____

b ure _____ _____

_____ _____

_____ _____

_____ _____

_____ _____

③ **Name.**

a _____   b _____

④ **Word clues.** Which list word means?

a an area where boats can anchor _____

b a kind act that is helpful to someone _____

c an exciting journey or activity _____

d a small hole _____

e plants, animals, the Earth _____

f a smell _____

Endings: or, ure

1 Revise your spelling list from page 109. Underline the spelling mistakes. Write the word correctly.

a   My bicycle tyre had a punctour.

b   The cake mixtour tasted delicious.

c   Our vacation was a great adventour.

d   We followed the treasour map at the pirate party.

e   They took a pictour at the top of the lookout.

f   The boat sailed away from the harbure and out to sea.

g   The huge structour will take years to build.

Challenge words

2 Write the word.

savior

procedure

behavior

manufacture

signature

literature

pressure

curvature

enclosure

architecture

3 Hidden words. Find the challenge word.

a   rearcurvaturecura

b   urepressurepres

c   reenclosureenslo

d   smanufacturefsfe

e   vdssignaturesdgs

f   sbehaviorfsdgfs

g   dfarchitecturedfgr

h   gliteraturesdgfg

i   ureprocedureproo

j   vioursaviorsavor

4 Word clues. Which challenge word matches?

a   a person who saves people from danger

b   stories, poems, plays, essays

c   used to sign documents

d   to make something

e   designing buildings

L.4.2.D Spell grade-appropriate words correctly.

Frequently confused words

Commonly confused words are words that sound or look similar, but which have different spellings and meanings. Many commonly confused words are homophones; e.g., I **knew** those shoes were **new**.

1 **Complete each sentence with words from the box.**

| threw   would   tied   breath   wood   breathe   quiet   through   tide   quite |

a Before you can _____ in, you have to let your _____ out.

b He _____ the paper airplane _____ the open doorway.

c I have never known that noisy child to be _____ so _____.

d If we had some _____ , I _____ use it to make the model.

e We _____ the boat to the dock before the _____ came in.

2 **Match the word to the definition.**

a hare   the colored part of a plant

b hair   in this place

c flour   in that place

d flower   to listen

e toe   like a rabbit

f tow   belonging to them

g hear   a digit on your foot

h here   something that grows on your head

i their   to pull

j there   used to make bread

3 **Underline the word that is wrong and write it correctly.**

a I hope to be a famous actor won day.   _____

b They introduced me to there parents.   _____

c I sore the mountains in the distance.   _____

d The house has fore large bedrooms.   _____

e I can't remember wear I put my ring.   _____

f The new boy didn't no what to do.   _____

The Creaky House Club

Read the passage.

In paragraph 1, (circle) two adjectives that describe how Sam was feeling.

Highlight the adjective that shows how Sam felt about keeping a secret from his friend.

At home, Sam looked at the kitchen clock. One hour to go. Part of him was excited but the rest of him was terrified. What if they did something really bad to him? Something where they didn't mean to hurt him, but it went wrong?

Sam knew there was no way out of it. He had to show up. He just wished that Tristan was coming too. He felt rotten about keeping it all from his friend. How was he going to tell Tristan if he did get into the Creaky House Club?

"I'll see you later, Dad," Sam called, as he left the house and cycled towards The Creaky House.

Underline the dialogue in the passage.

Circle the correct answer for each question.

1 Which option best describes this text? It is part of ...

    a an explanation.
    b a story.
    c a diary entry.
    d a set of instructions.

2 Based on your answer to question 1, what is the main purpose of the text?

    a to inform
    b to persuade
    c to warn
    d to entertain

3 What can we **infer** about Sam and Tristan? Sam and Tristan are ...

    a at preschool.
    b kindergartners.
    c in elementary school.
    d at university.

4 Who is the most likely audience for this text?

    a under 5s
    b adults
    c 8–12 year-olds
    d cyclists

RL.4.1 Refer to details and examples in a text when explaining what the text says explicitly and when drawing inferences from the text.

The Creaky House Club

Read the whole story

Creaky House Club

Read the passage.

A voice that sounded familiar said, "Welcome to The Creaky House Club, Sam. As you know, we select our members very carefully. Firstly, we'd like to know why you want to join our club?"

Sam had thought they'd ask him this question, but he still didn't have a good answer.

"Well ... I'm a good basketball player and I'd like to be part of the most popular group in school at the moment," said Sam.

"At the moment?" came the reply. "What do you mean 'at the moment'?"

"I've goofed already," Sam thought. But aloud he said, "Well, at the moment and in the future I mean."

1 **Who** is Sam talking to? _____

2 What does the **dialogue suggest** about the kind of text this is?

_____

_____

3 What is the **main reason** authors write these types of text?

_____

_____

4 Who do you think the **target audience** is for this text? Give a reason/s for your answer.

_____

_____

_____

RL.4.1 Refer to details and examples in a text when explaining what the text says explicitly and when drawing inferences from the text.

Digraphs: wh, ph, gh

A **digraph** is two consonants that make a single sound.
The consonants **wh**, make the sound **w**; e.g., **wh**iff.
The consonants **gh**, make the sound **g**; e.g., **gh**ostly.
The consonants **ph**, make the sound **f**; e.g., **ph**armacy.

List **①** **Write the word.**

which _____
whim _____
phrase _____
whiff _____
sphere _____
whisk _____
whack _____
whine _____
ghostly _____
pamphlet _____
whilst _____
spaghetti _____
whiskers _____
pharmacy _____
whinny _____
orphan _____
whereas _____
hyphen _____
alphabet _____
graphic _____

② **Name.**

a _____   b _____

③ **Missing digraphs.** Write the missing digraphs.

a _____iskers   b _____ilst
c _____ine   d _____ack
e _____ostly   f _____rase
g _____im   h _____iff
i _____ereas   j s_____ere
k hy_____en   l pam_____let
m _____ich   n spa_____etti
o _____isk   p gra_____ic
q _____armacy   r _____inny
s al_____abet   t or_____an

④ **Sort the words.**

wh	gh	ph

L.4.2.D Spell grade-appropriate words correctly.

Digraphs: wh, ph, gh

1 **Revise your spelling list from page 114.** Which list word means?

a   the noise a horse makes _____

b   the 26 letters used in English _____

c   long, thin pasta _____

d   a round 3D object _____

e   a cooking utensil used to blend ingredients _____

f   a place to buy medicine _____

g   someone who no longer has parents _____

Challenge words

2 **Write the word.**

overwhelm _____

apostrophe _____

atmosphere _____

prophet _____

aghast _____

phlegm _____

sapphire _____

biography _____

worthwhile _____

phoenix _____

3 **Word clues.** Which challenge word means?

a   a punctuation mark _____

b   filled with horror _____

c   story of someone's life _____

d   deep blue gemstone _____

e   overpower _____

f   gases around earth _____

g   a mythical bird _____

h   thick mucus _____

i   one who predicts the future

_____

4 **Complete the sentence.**

a   Getting a pay raise made all the hard work _____.

b   The Earth's _____ absorbs part of the sun's light.

c   A _____ is a mythical bird that is reborn from its own ashes.

d   I bought medicine to help break up the _____ in my throat.

e   My grandmother's ring has a large _____ in the middle.

Reported speech

> **Reported speech** is when someone reports **what someone else has said without using their exact words**; e.g., My mother said she would make us a cake.

1 Check (✔) examples of reported speech.

a "What's that?" asked Ross. ☐ b He said he would give her the note. ☐

c She said she would be there. ☐ d She said that her foot was sore. ☐

e He told us to stop talking. ☐ f "I hurt it yesterday," she said. ☐

g "Sit down," the man said. ☐ h "Where are my socks?" he asked. ☐

i She said she was very tired. ☐ j Max said he hadn't seen them. ☐

k Min said, "That's my bag." ☐ l Bella told him they were on the chair. ☐

2 Complete the second sentence with the correct pronoun.

a Olivia asked Tom, "What are you going to make with the wood?"
Olivia asked Tom what _____ was going to make with the wood.

b "We saw Lena at the museum," said Aaron and Angelina.
Aaron and Angelina said _____ saw Lena at the museum.

c "I won't say a word," promised Sophia.
Sophia promised that _____ wouldn't say a word.

d "My tooth is sore," complained the boy.
The boy complained that _____ tooth was sore.

3 Complete the second sentence using reported speech.

a "It's time to go home," Dad told the children.
Dad told the children that _____

_____

b "When are you leaving?" the man asked.
The man asked us _____

_____

L.4.2.B Use commas and quotation marks to mark quotations from a text.

The Woman and the Corn

Making inferences
Use clues in the text to make inferences (form opinions). The clues will help you find the answers that are hiding in the text.

Read the passage.

Underline who Miya's father was.

Highlight what the voice offered to do.

Put a box around the type of country Miya traveled through.

Narrator: Once upon a time, there lived a young woman called Miya. Her father was lord of his people. One day, Miya was swimming in the river when she heard a voice.

Miya: What was that? Who's there?

Narrator: The voice said it would lead her to the man of her dreams, if she followed it.

Miya: The man of my dreams! I would love to be married to him!

Narrator: So Miya followed the voice as best she could through the jungle until she reached a cave.

Circle the correct answer for each question.

1 What **inference** can we make about the voice? It belonged to …
- a the man of Miya's dreams.
- b someone Miya couldn't see.
- c Miya's father.
- d an animal.

2 What is the **clue** to question 1's answer? In the text it states that Miya followed …
- a the man.
- b the woman.
- c the shadowy figure.
- d the voice.

3 What **inference** can we make about what Miya mainly saw on her way to the cave? Miya most likely saw lots of …
- a trees.
- b deserts.
- c mountains.
- d oceans.

4 Which word is the **clue** to question 3's answer?
- a cave
- b jungle
- c dreams
- d voice

The Woman and the Corn

Read the passage.

Underline the reason Jose came to see Miya.

Color the welcome the villagers gave Miya.

Narrator: One day Jose, a farmer from Miya's village, appeared at the cave.

Jose: Miya? Miya? Are you there? There is a famine and we have no food. We are starving. Help us!

Miya: <to Lord of the Bats> My husband, I love you but I must leave and return to my village. The villagers need me.

Narrator: So Miya and Jose returned to their village, but Miya did not receive a hero's welcome.

Miya's father: Stop right there! We are hungry because of you, Miya. It is your fault we have no corn.

Narrator: Miya was very upset and returned to the Lord of the Bats.

Lord of the Bats: Don't cry, Miya, because you can still help your village. This is what you must do.

Highlight what Miya's father said to her.

Put a box around how Miya felt after her father spoke to her.

1 What can we **infer** about the kind of person Miya is? Support your answer with evidence from the text.

_____

_____

_____

2 What can we **infer** about the kind of person the Lord of the Bats is? Support your answer with evidence from the text.

_____

_____

_____

_____

RL.4.1 Refer to details and examples in a text when explaining what the text says explicitly and when drawing inferences from the text.

Vowel sound y

The letter **y** can be a consonant or a vowel sound. In many words that come from Greek, **y** makes a short **i** sound; e.g., m**y**th, s**y**rup.

List

gym
hymn
myth
lyric
Egypt
syrup
system
crystal
bicycle
syllable
gymnastics
cygnet
mystery
pyramid
oxygen
typical
physical
symbol
symptom
rhythm

① Write the word.

② Unscramble these list words.

a ystermy
b scitsanmyg
c mnyh
d ygnoxe
e ystsme
f lyalsebl
g mlbsoy
h sycrlat
i ciryl

③ In a group. Write the list words that belong in each group.

a exercise, aerobics, gym, _____
b mummies, pharaoh, Egypt, _____
c legend, fairy tale, _____
d mineral, gem, _____
e hydrogen, carbon dioxide, _____
f swan, duck, _____
g song, poem, _____
h puzzle, secret, _____

④ Meaning. Which list word means?

a A baby swan
b A traditional story usually containing unusual characters
c A sign that you are ill
d Huge stone structures built as tombs in Egypt
e A small vehicle with two wheels, pedals, and a handle bar
f A place that helps improve or maintain your physical health

Vowel sound y

1 **Revise your spelling list from page 119.** Underline the spelling mistakes. Write the word correctly.

a We breathe in oxigen and breathe out carbon dioxide. _____

b Genevieve wrote a lyrik poem about her pet cat. _____

c The largest piramid in Giza used about 2.3 million stone blocks. _____

d I like to use the rowing machines at the gim. _____

e My mom's most precious drinking glasses are made of cristal. _____

f I was reading a mysterie novel and didn't want to stop. _____

g My sore throat was a symptome of my cold. _____

h The sphinx and the pyramids are ancient wonders of Egypte. _____

Challenge words

2 **Write the word.**

crypt

cryptic _____

mythical _____

cymbal _____

antonym _____

hypocrite _____

symphony _____

symbolic _____

calypso _____

hypnotize _____

3 **Word clues.** Which challenge word means?

a concert orchestra _____

b burial chamber _____

c the opposite meaning

_____

d percussion instrument

_____

e to mesmerize _____

f hidden meaning _____

g music of the West Indies

_____

h a person who says one thing and does another

_____

4 **Complete the sentence.**

a Our band is looking for someone to play the _____.

b They buried the son of the king in the royal _____.

c Happy is the _____ of sad.

d The color red is often _____ of anger or danger.

L.4.2.D Spell grade-appropriate words correctly.

Punctuating quotations

A **quotation** is what someone has said or writing taken from someone/somewhere else. The **quoted words**, plus any punctuation, are placed between **quotation marks** (" "); e.g., Ralph Waldo Emerson once said, "The only way to have a friend is to be one."

1 **In the following sentences, underline the quoted words.**

a The motto for the Olympic Games is "Faster, Higher, Stronger."

b On the back of the girl's T-shirt were the words, "Earth Matters."

c In *Charlie and the Chocolate Factory*, Roald Dahl advises us to fill our shelves "with lots of books."

d The writer, Hans Christian Andersen, once wrote that "Life itself is the most wonderful fairy tale."

e "Fall seven times, stand up eight" is a famous Japanese proverb.

2 **In the following sentences, fill in the quotation marks.**

a Our quote of the day is, Today a reader, tomorrow a leader.

b One of my favorite quotes from Dr. Seuss is, You can find magic wherever you look.

c The sun does arise is the first line of a poem by William Blake.

d When Joe shouted, Watch out! everyone ducked.

e The last thing his grandson said was, When will I see you again?

3 **In the following sentences, fill in the missing punctuation.**

a Thomas Edison, inventor of the light bulb, said of his achievements, I never did a day's work in my life. It was all fun

b The United Nations Convention on the Rights of the Child states that Children have the right to an education

c When I asked Mom what it was like to have the best daughter in the world, she said, I don't know, dear. You'll have to ask Grandma

L.4.1 Demonstrate command of the conventions of standard English grammar and usage when writing or speaking.

121

The Young Lion King

Important information
To find the most important information in a text, look for the words, phrases, or sentences that tell us the most about the subject.

Read the passage.

Underline the reason Lion King did not think Fox would make a good teacher.

Highlight the reason Lion King did not choose Mole.

Lion King wondered which animal could teach the Lion Prince. He wondered if Fox could do it. Fox, though clever, was a great liar and liars always cause trouble. He wondered about Mole. Mole was orderly and careful but never looked far ahead. The King wondered about Panther. Panther was strong, brave, and a great fighter, but liked fighting a little too much. The Lion knew that a good king is just, wise, and can solve things without fighting.

Put a box around the things Lion King liked about Panther.

Color the reason Lion King did not want Panther to teach Lion Prince.

Circle the correct answer/s for each question.

1 Which three animals did Lion King think of when looking for a teacher for the Lion Prince?

a Fox   b Panther   c Wolf

d Mole   e Bear   f Snake

2 Which three sentences give the most information about why Lion King **did not** choose those animals?

a He did not think Fox could do it.

b Fox, though clever, was a great liar and liars always cause trouble.

c He wondered about mole.

d Mole was orderly and careful but never looked far ahead.

e The King wondered about Panther.

f Panther was strong, brave, and a great fighter, but liked fighting a little too much.

The Young Lion King

Read the passage.

Circle the animal Lion King chose to teach his son.

Highlight what the Lion Prince had learned.

Lion was still thinking when Eagle flew by. "Of course!" Lion cried. "Eagle!" The Lion King sent his son to study at Eagle's court.

Years later, Lion Prince returned to his father, in time to take over his kingdom.

"Father," said the Lion Prince, "I have learned many things. I can tell where every bird can find water. I know what kind of food each bird needs. I know how many eggs it lays and the wants of every bird that flies. When I am in charge of the kingdom, I shall begin to teach our animals how to build nests."

The animals in the King's court howled with laughter. The King realized the Lion Prince had not been taught the knowledge a great king needs most of all—a knowledge of the wants and needs of his own people and land.

Color what the other animals did when they heard what Lion Prince had learned.

Underline the information that the Lion Prince needed most of all.

1. Eagle taught Lion Prince the things he would need to know if he were going to rule the bird kingdom. What **important information** did Eagle give the young prince?

a _____

b _____

c _____

d _____

2. **What** should the Lion Prince have learned?

_____

_____

_____

_____

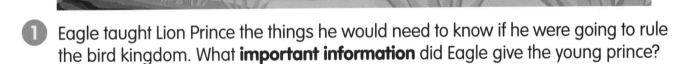

RL.4.1 Refer to details and examples in a text when explaining what the text says explicitly and when drawing inferences from the text.

123

Digraph: ch

Two or more letters that make a single sound are called a **digraph**.
The letters **ch** sometimes make the **ch** sound; e.g., **ch**imps.
The letters **ch** can also make the **k** sound; e.g., **ch**oir.
Sometimes the letters ch can make the **sh** sound; e.g., **ch**ef.

List **1** **Write the word.**

bleach
coach
chunk
chapter
chef
chime
echo
chore
choose
chance
chuckle
enchant
chord
chute
chemist
chorus
cheetah
chubby
Christmas
archery

2 **Name.**

a _____   b _____

3 **Unscramble these list words.**

a tmcishe
b tcheann
c prcthae
d hechaet
e belhac
f hacryre
g kcuhlce
h fche
i bcubhy
j uchros

4 **Meaning.** Which list word means?

a Musical notes played together
b Sound waves bouncing back from a surface
c Titled or numbered section of a book
d A chemical used to make things clean or white
e To charm or fill someone with delight
f A section of a song that is repeated after the verse

Digraph: ch

1 **Revise your spelling list from page 124.** Which word? Complete the sentences with the list words.

a I could hear the voice of our _____ _____ across the field. (coach, echo)

b He could _____ his audience with a single _____. (chord, enchant)

c The _____ took a _____ from the zebra's leg. (chunk, cheetah)

d I decided to _____ _____ over rock climbing. (archery, choose)

e _____ shopping can often feel like a _____. (Christmas, chore)

Challenge words

2 **Write the word.**

choir _____

chasm _____

chivalry _____

chocolate _____

anchor _____

character _____

parachute _____

chronicle _____

chaos _____

chandelier _____

3 **Word clues.** Which challenge word means?

a deep crack in the earth

_____

b used to stop boats moving

_____

c events recorded in order

_____

d hangs from the ceiling

_____

e courage, honor, virtue

_____

f made from cacao

_____

4 **Complete the sentence.**

a I got angry when my brother ate the whole block of _____.

b They dropped supplies into the disaster area by _____.

c The choirmaster organized the _____, with sopranos on the right.

d They built a bridge over the _____.

e There was _____ when a spider fell on Dad's head.

f The soldier wrote a _____ of his time in the war.

g We were so glad the _____ didn't fall during the quake.

Modal auxiliaries

A **modal auxiliary** shows if something is possible, certain, or necessary; e.g.,
- I might go. (possible)
- I will go. (certain)
- You must hurry. (necessary)

1 **Do the underlined auxiliaries show certainty or possibility?**

a They <u>can't</u> solve the problem.   _____

b I <u>will</u> meet you at the bus stop.   _____

c We <u>may</u> see them at the beach tomorrow.   _____

d I <u>won't</u> finish my project on time.   _____

e My friend <u>might</u> be waiting for me.   _____

f I <u>can</u> write neatly when I want to.   _____

g We <u>might not</u> be going in the right direction. _____

2 **Complete each sentence with a modal auxiliary from the box. Use each one once.**

won't	will	may	must	might	can't

a I _____ know her, but I'm not sure.

b I _____ definitely try harder next time.

c I _____ let the little girl out of my sight.

d If you want to win, you _____ train harder.

e That _____ be my pencil, but I _____ be certain.

3 **Use the word at the end of the sentence to help you choose the correct modal.**

a The teacher (might, will) _____ be in the library.   (possible)

b The children (may, must) _____ be in bed by eight.   (necessary)

c The penguins (won't, may not) _____ be at the zoo.   (certain)

d I (will, may) _____ be able to help you tomorrow.   (possible)

L.4.1.C Use modal auxiliaries.

Forces

Read the passage.

Circle the cause of earthquakes, wind, and waves.

Underline what happens when plates push against each other and pull apart.

Highlight what happens to warm air.

Color the words that show the difference between earth tremors and earthquakes.

Forces cause earthquakes, wind, and waves in and on the Earth.

The Earth's surface is made up of large, slow-moving plates of rock. The plates push against each other and pull apart. This releases energy, which causes the land above the plates to move. This might be an earth tremor that you can't feel or a violent earthquake.

Wind is caused by changes in air pressure. When warm air rises, cooler, heavier air rushes in to fill the space. This moving air is called wind.

Ocean waves are caused by the force of the wind.

Circle the correct answer for each question.

1 How are earth tremors and earthquakes **similar**? Both are caused by ...

a changes in air pressure.
b moving plates of rock.
c violent winds.
d the Earth's gravitational pull.

2 How are earth tremors and earthquakes **different**? Earth tremors are ...

a stronger than earthquakes.
b louder than earthquakes.
c weaker than earthquakes.
d bigger than earthquakes.

3 How are wind and waves **similar**? Both are caused by ...

a forces.
b warm air.
c slow-moving plates of rock.
d gravity.

4 How are warm air and cool air **different**? Warm air is ...

a dirtier than cool air.
b thicker than cool air.
c saltier than cool air.
d lighter than cool air.

Forces

Read the passage.

Underline the force that sends the ball toward the net.

Circle the force that slows the ball down.

Color the force that pulls the ball down.

When a basketball player shoots, a push force sends the ball toward the net. Friction with the air slows the ball down. Gravity pulls it back toward the court. The ball would just keep going up without the action of these forces.

An aircraft has four forces acting on it. The engines produce a forward force, called thrust. The wings produce an upward force called lift. Friction from air rushing over the aircraft, called drag, slows it down. Gravity pulls it toward the earth.

What happens to an object depends on the sum of all the forces acting on it. The basketball reaches the net because the force of the shot is greater than the effects of gravity and friction. The aircraft moves forward because the thrust from the engines is greater than gravity and drag.

Highlight the force produced by an aircraft's wings.

Circle the force that slows the aircraft down.

Color the force that pulls the aircraft down.

1 **Which force** causes both the ball and the aircraft to **slow down**?

_____

_____

2 **Which force** causes both the ball and the aircraft to return to Earth?

_____

_____

3 **Explain** the reason:

a   the basketball **reaches the net**. _____

_____

b   the aircraft **moves forward**. _____

_____

RI.4.1 Refer to details and examples in a text when explaining what the text says explicitly and when drawing inferences from the text.

Endings: in, ine, ain

Some words that end in the **n sound** have the letters **in** at the end; e.g., cab**in**.

Some words that end in the **n sound** have the letters **ine** at the end; e.g., imag**ine**.

Some words that end in the **n sound** have the letters **ain** at the end; e.g., barg**ain**.

List **1** **Write the word.**

cousin _____

dolphin _____

raisin _____

engine _____

famine _____

mountain _____

captain _____

basin _____

robin _____

cabin _____

violin _____

vitamin _____

certain _____

pumpkin _____

curtain _____

napkin _____

margin _____

bargain _____

imagine _____

villain _____

2 **Name.**

a _____   b _____

3 **Chunks.** Rearrange the chunks to make a list word.

a in b ro _____

b mp kin pu _____

c ine m fa _____

d in dol ph _____

e ta min vi _____

f ill ain v _____

g g ain bar _____

h rt ain cu _____

i ne en gi _____

j ma i gi ne _____

4 **Sort the words.**

in		ine	ain

Endings: in, ine, ain

1 **Revise your spelling list from page 129.** Which list word means?

a   A mammal that lives in water

b   Extreme shortage of food over a large area

c   An evil person who causes trouble for the hero

d   A machine that turns fuel or electricity into power

e   A grape that has been partially dried out

f   A bird with a red breast

Challenge words

2 **Write the word.**

origin

examine

medicine

genuine

javelin

chieftain

penguin

feminine

porcelain

discipline

3 **Word clues.** Which challenge word means?

a   flightless bird

b   white, shiny pottery

c   opposite of masculine

d   pointed pole

e   to study or investigate

f   the leader of a tribe

g   given to a sick person

h   where something begins

4 **Another way to say it.** Which challenge word could replace the underlined words?

a   I go to the art museum to <u>study</u> the paintings.

b   The doctor was very careful to give the correct <u>treatment</u>.

c   The <u>ruler</u> of the tribe always acts fairly.

d   It takes hard work and <u>a strict routine</u> to train and compete in marathons.

e   I threw the <u>spear</u> the furthest.

f   We were to investigate the <u>beginning</u> of the First World War.

L.4.2.D Spell grade-appropriate words correctly.

Subjects and predicates

Sentences can be divided into subjects and predicates. The **subject** is the **person or thing** that the sentence is about; e.g., Little Red Riding Hood. The predicate is the rest of the sentence, including the verb; e.g., **Little Red Riding Hood** met a wolf in the forest.

1 **Complete each sentence with a subject from the box.**

a _____ was fixing the pipe when I arrived.

b _____ is in the garage.

c _____ should open the cupboard door.

d _____ are coming to my house this afternoon.

e _____ have to take turns on the computer.

My brother and I   Their new car   My friends   This little key   The plumber

2 **Put a box around the subjects and underline the predicates.**

a The bees are collecting pollen from the flowers.

b The very hungry caterpillar ate everything in sight.

c The largest building on the street is the post office.

d A few children in my ballet class are going to the beach tomorrow.

3 **Match the subjects and predicates.**

Subject	Predicate
a That large white animal	was built a long time ago.
b The house on the corner	are coming to my party.
c The author's latest book	licked my hand.
d The cute little dog	is a polar bear.
e All of my friends	is in the library.

People and the Sea

Read the passage.

Making inferences
Use the clues in the text to make inferences (form opinions). The clues will help you find the answers that are hiding in the text.

Underline the main reason people set sail in early times.

Circle what people used to think the Earth looked like.

Color the reasons some ships sank.

From early times people have set sail on the oceans to explore the unknown. Some explorers looked for new lands to settle. Others looked for fame, treasure, or adventure.

Long before science helped us understand the oceans, people thought the Earth was flat. Sailors believed that if they sailed far enough, they would fall off the edge of the world. Of course they never did, but storms, pirates, and hidden reefs meant that some ships did sink to the bottom of the sea. Today, adventurers go in search of sunken treasure!

Circle the correct answer for each question.

1. What can we **infer** about early explorers?
   a. They all wanted to find new lands.
   b. They all hoped to find treasure.
   c. They went to sea for different reasons.
   d. They all found fame and fortune.

2. Which two words are the best **clues** to question 1's answer?
   a. *explore* and *unknown*
   b. *Some* and *Others*
   c. *lands* and *settle*
   d. *sail* and *oceans*

3. What can we **infer** about some of the old ships that sank?
   a. They contained treasure.
   b. They were steam ships.
   c. They fell off the edge of the world.
   d. They didn't sail far enough out to sea.

4. Which sentence is the best **clue** to question 3's answer?
   a. Others looked for fame, treasure, or adventure.
   b. Some explorers looked for new lands to settle.
   c. Sailors believed that they would fall off the edge of the world.
   d. Today, adventurers go in search of sunken treasure!

RI.4.1 Refer to details and examples in a text when explaining what the text says explicitly and when drawing inferences from the text.

People and the Sea

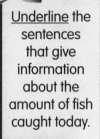

Read the full text

People and the Sea

Read the passage.

People have always caught fish and other sea creatures using baskets, hooks, and nets. Today large fishing boats can catch, clean, and freeze fish while still at sea.

Modern fishing boats take huge amounts of seafood from the sea. Popular ocean fish that people eat include tuna, herring, sardines, cod, and snapper. Every year about 75 million tons of fish are caught worldwide.

Seaweed is also harvested. People eat it raw or cooked and sometimes use it to thicken foods such as ice cream and yogurt. Seaweed can also be used to make toothpaste and sausages!

1 We can **infer** that there are different methods of catching fish. What evidence is there in the text to support this statement?

_____

_____

2 We can **infer** that more fish are caught today than were caught in the past. What evidence is there in the text to support this statement?

_____

_____

_____

3 Based on the information in paragraph 3, what can we **infer** about seaweed?

_____

_____

_____

Suffix: ous

Adding the suffix **ous** to a noun or verb turns it into an adjective; e.g., danger → danger**ous**.
If the base word ends in **e**, drop the e before adding **ous**; e.g., fame → fam**ous**.
If the base word ends in **y** and there is a <u>consonant before</u> the **y**, change the y to i before adding **ous**; e.g., glor**y** → glor**ious**.
Some adjectives that end in **ous** are not formed from verbs or nouns; e.g., serious.

List
1 Write the word.

nervous _____
famous _____
jealous _____
fabulous _____
dangerous _____
serious _____
previous _____
curious _____
obvious _____
furious _____
precious _____
various _____
cautious _____
generous _____
tremendous _____
mysterious _____
glamorous _____
adventurous _____
humorous _____
delicious _____

2 **Syllables.** Rearrange the syllables to make a list word.

a ger ous dan _____
b dous tre men _____
c pre ous vi _____
d er ous gen _____
e vous ner _____

3 **Missing letter.** Fill in the missing letters.

a dan _ er _ _ s   **b** fu _ _ _ us
c _ reme _ _ _ us   **d** s _ ri _ _ _
e v _ rio _ _   **f** de _ ic _ _ _ _
g mys _ _ rio _ _   **h** _ bvi _ _ _
i cur _ o _ _   **j** ca _ t _ _ _ _
k j _ alo _ _   **l** _ en _ _ o _ _
m adven _ u _ _ _ _   **n** f _ b _ l _ _ _
o gl _ mor _ _ _   **p** p _ eci _ _ _
q _ u _ _ ro _ _   **r** ner _ _ _ _

4 **Meaning.** Which list word means?

a Something of great value or worth _____
b Having many different features _____
c Recognized or known by many people _____
d Something not safe; likely to cause harm _____
e Eager to know or learn something _____
f Something that is easily seen, perceived, or understood _____

L.4.2.D Spell grade-appropriate words correctly.

Suffix: ous

1 **Revise your spelling list from page 134.** Complete each sentence with a list word.

a I got very _____ before speaking at the assembly.

b As the guest I was given a _____ serving of dessert.

c I thought his joke was very _____.

d I placed my watch in an _____ place so I wouldn't forget it for the big race.

e Mom's homemade pancakes were simply _____.

f You must be extra _____ when crossing busy roads.

g Our _____ coach was much nicer than our new one.

Challenge words

2 **Write the word.**

hideous   _____

prosperous   _____

ridiculous   _____

disastrous   _____

gorgeous   _____

spacious   _____

luxurious   _____

anxious   _____

precarious   _____

treacherous _____

3 **Complete the sentence.**

a Low rainfall means that farmers will be _____ this year.

b He was in a _____ position standing on the tree branch.

c On our vacation we stayed at a _____ hotel.

d The _____ soldier told the enemy the position of his army.

e "They are _____!" said Johnny about the orange and green striped cushions.

4 **Another way to say it.** Which challenge word could replace the underlined words?

a The <u>terrible</u> cyclone has destroyed most of this year's crops. _____

b Wearing a cat as a hat is just plain <u>silly</u>. _____

c I was sent a <u>beautiful</u> bouquet of roses on my birthday. _____

d Our new house is very <u>large</u>. _____

e I found a <u>revolting</u> toad swimming in our pool. _____

Correctly punctuate run-on sentences

A **run-on sentence** occurs when two **main clauses** are **joined without any punctuation**, or with the **wrong punctuation**; e.g., I love pizza I could eat it every day. I love pizza, I could eat it every day. The correct punctuation to separate the clauses is a **period**; e.g., I love pizza. I could eat it every day.

1 In each of the following pairs, check (✔) the sentence that has the correct punctuation.

a   The hikers took the wrong path. They got lost. ☐

b   The hikers took the wrong path they got lost. ☐

c   The hikers had enough food. They were running out of water. ☐

d   The hikers had enough food, they were running out of water. ☐

e   The hikers reached a camp they filled their water bottles. ☐

f   The hikers reached a camp. They filled their water bottles. ☐

2 Write each run-on sentence as two separate sentences.

a   I got a kitten for my birthday, I was so happy.

_____

_____

b   We knew it would rain soon, the clouds were getting darker and heavier.

_____

_____

3 Correct the following run-on sentences by joining the clauses with *and* or *but*.

a   I dropped the stone in the pond, it sank to the bottom.

_____

_____

b   I put new batteries in the toy, it still didn't work.

_____

_____

   L.4.1.F Produce complete sentences, recognizing and correcting inappropriate fragments and run-ons.

How Big Is Your Carbon Footprint?

Cause and effect
To find cause and effect, ask why something happens and what the result is.

Read the passage.

Underline the reason many scientists say temperatures are rising.

Highlight where ice is melting.

Circle the cause of the melting ice.

Most scientists believe that we should be concerned about global warming. Firstly, they say measurements taken on Earth and in space show that the average temperature is getting higher. They attribute this rise in temperature to the gases released into the atmosphere when fossil fuels are burned. Secondly, the warmer temperatures are causing vast chunks of ice to melt around the north and south poles, resulting in rising sea levels. This could lead to coastal areas and low-lying land being swamped.

Finally, they point to the shrinking of glaciers in many parts of the world.

Color what could happen if sea levels continue to rise.

Put a box around how rising temperatures are affecting glaciers.

Circle the correct answer for each question.

1 According to most scientists, what is **causing** temperatures to rise?

a storms on the sun
b earthquakes and volcanoes
c disappearing rainforests
d burning fossil fuels

2 According to most scientists, what **effect** are gases from burning fossil fuels having on the earth? They are **causing** ...

a temperatures to fall.
b temperatures to rise.
c lots of thunderstorms.
d earthquakes and volcanoes.

3 What **could happen** if sea levels continue to rise?

a Swamps will form.
b The land will rise with the water.
c Coastal areas will be swamped.
d The continents will break up.

4 What do most scientists believe is **causing** glaciers to shrink?

a rising temperatures
b heavy rainfall
c not enough rainfall
d strong winds

L.4.4.A Use context (e.g., definitions, examples, or restatements in text) as a clue to the meaning of a word or phrase.

How Big Is Your Carbon Footprint?

Read the passage.

Highlight the key phrase that tells us what some scientists believe about global warming.

<u>Underline</u> what some scientists blame global warming on.

But there are some scientists who believe that global warming is a natural process that has been happening for the last 6,000 years. The average temperature today, they say, is approximately 11 degrees warmer than it was back then, but it has been rising gradually since that time, not suddenly in the last 100 years. These scientists blame global warming on the way our planets are aligned and the effect they have on our orbit, and that is something we have no control over.

As for me, I have always preferred to err on the side of caution, so I will continue to switch off lights and do whatever I can to reduce my carbon footprint on the planet.

Color what the author is going to continue doing.

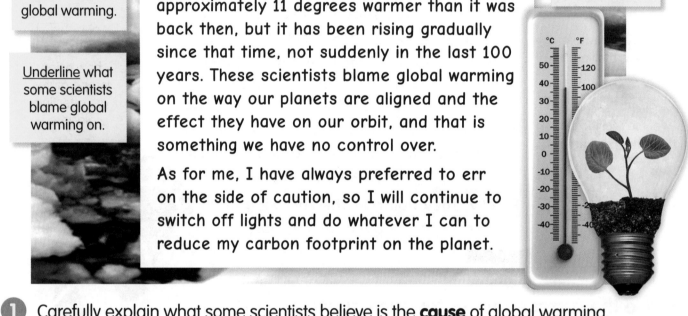

1 Carefully explain what some scientists believe is the **cause** of global warming.

_____
_____
_____
_____
_____
_____

2 What **effect** does the author believe his or her actions might have on the environment?

_____
_____
_____
_____

L.4.4.A Use context (e.g., definitions, examples, or restatements in text) as a clue to the meaning of a word or phrase.

Prefixes: in, im, ir, il

Adding the **prefix in** to a word can turn it into its opposite; e.g., correct → **in**correct.

If a word **starts** with **b**, **m** or **p**, use **im** instead of **in**; e.g., **b**alance → **im**balance, **m**obile → **im**mobile, **p**ossible → **im**possible.

If a word **starts** with **r**, use **ir**; e.g., **r**egular → **ir**regular.

If a word **starts** with **l**, use **il**; e.g., **l**egal → **il**legal.

List ① Write the word.

inactive _____

invisible _____

impure _____

immobile _____

incomplete _____

impolite _____

insecure _____

irregular _____

incorrect _____

imperfect _____

inaccurate _____

incurable _____

impossible _____

infertile _____

impatient _____

illegal _____

immature _____

immortal _____

illogical _____

impersonal _____

② Chunks. Rearrange the chunks to make a list word.

a mo im bi le _____

b cu ra in ble _____

c e ill gal _____

d com ple in te _____

e vi ble si in _____

f po te li im _____

g se in re cu _____

③ Unscramble these list words.

a tcefrepmi _____

b lglelia _____

c iuenctacar _____

d inbercaul _____

e pmlisareon _____

f elbissopmi _____

g ilevnsibi _____

h metiumar _____

④ Sort the words.

in	im	ir	il

Prefixes: in, im, ir, il

1 **Revise your spelling list from page 139.** Underline the spelling mistakes. Write the word correctly.

a The contestant gave an imcorrect answer on the final question. _____

b My fear of cockroaches was inllogical, but I was still afraid. _____

c If I could have one superpower, I would like to be ilvisible. _____

d The criminal was arrested for his imllegal dealings. _____

e The rain fell at inrregular intervals throughout the day. _____

f I do not like people who are rude and inpolite. _____

g The crowd was restless and ilpatient for the show to start. _____

Challenge words

2 **Write the word.**

irrelevant _____
imbalance _____
improbable _____
impractical _____
insincere _____
irresponsible _____
illiterate _____
illegible _____
impartial _____
irreplaceable _____

3 **Word clues.** Which challenge word means?

a fair _____

b not meaning what you say _____

c difficult to read _____

d lack of balance _____

e cannot be exchanged _____

f of little or no importance _____

g something that is not useful _____

h unable to read or write _____

4 **Another way to say it.** Which challenge word could replace the underlined word?

a I could tell that he was being <u>dishonest</u>. _____

b Riding a bike without a helmet is extremely <u>reckless</u>. _____

c Her writing is <u>unreadable</u>, so I don't know what she wrote. _____

d It is highly <u>unlikely</u> that it will snow in Miami. _____

e It was <u>unrealistic</u> of me to bring a bathing suit to the snow. _____

Simple and compound sentences

A sentence is a group of words that makes complete sense. A **simple sentence** has **one subject** and **one verb**, so it contains one clause; e.g., The kitten is playing with the ball. A **compound sentence** contains **two clauses**, each of which can stand on its own. The clauses are **often joined** with conjunctions; e.g., Dogs can run, **but** they can't talk.

1 Complete each compound sentence with a conjunction from the list.

a The video was interesting, _____ I watched it again.

b She sat near the front, _____ she still couldn't see.

c It's a small car, _____ it has a powerful engine.

d A pelican is a bird, _____ a grasshopper is an insect.

so
but
and
yet

2 Circle the conjunction in each sentence.

a She can drive a car, but she can't ride a bicycle.

b They are very rich, yet they live in a small house.

c The apples were rotten, so we threw them away.

d You can read a magazine, or you can draw a picture.

3 Underline the clauses in these sentences.

a I was feeling sick, so I went to the doctor.

b She wanted a red bike, but they were sold out.

c You can have a smartphone, or you can have a laptop.

d I carried the groceries into the kitchen and he unpacked them.

4 Is it a simple sentence, or a compound sentence?

a I baked the cake and my sister iced it. _____

b The museum is in the center of the city. _____

c I went to the concert with my best friend. _____

d I gave him a candy, but he hasn't eaten it. _____

Coral Reefs

Read the passage.

Word study
Use clues in the text to work out the meaning of words you do not understand.

Underline words that explain what camouflage is.

Color the reason some fish change color.

Many reef fish have bright colors. This provides them with good camouflage. Colorful spots and stripes make them difficult to see among the coral. Some fish can even change their color to hide from predators. Others, such as trumpetfish, are predators that change color to trick their prey.

Put a box around the reason some predators change color.

Circle the correct answer/s for each question.

1 Which **best** describes what camouflage is?

   a scales   b a disguise   c color   d speed

2 Which phrase is the **clue** to question 1's answer?

   a bright colors   b Colorful spots and stripes

   c trick their prey   d make them difficult to see

3 Which **best** describes a predator?

   a a hunter   b a victim   c an old fish   d a large fish

4 What are the **two best clues** to question 3's answer? Some fish ...

   a have to hide from predators.

   b have bright colors.

   c are predators that change color to trick their prey.

   d have good camouflage.

5 Which word in the passage is the **opposite** of predator?

   a fish   b spots   c trick   d prey

L.4.4.A Use context (e.g., definitions, examples, or restatements in text) as a clue to the meaning of a word or phrase.

Coral Reefs

Read the passage.

Read the
full text

Coral Reefs

Highlight words that help us work out the meaning of *fragile*.

Color what happens when there are no longer any trees to protect the ground.

Coral reefs are fragile and they need to be protected. There are some natural threats to coral reefs, but people cause the most damage.

Coral needs clear water to grow. When forests are cut down on land, erosion washes soil into the ocean. The plants inside the corals stop growing and the corals begin to die.

Pollution caused by industry and shipping can also poison coral polyps. Ships leak fuel into the water and boat anchors break off coral. Oil spills can cause huge damage as well.

Underline how ships damage coral.

1 What does the phrase *need to be protected* suggest about the meaning of the word "fragile"?

_____

_____

2 Use the **clues** in paragraph 2 to help you write a definition for erosion.

_____

_____

3 Use the **clues** in paragraph 3 to help you write a definition for pollution.

_____

_____

_____

Suffixes: ion, ation

> Some verbs that **end** in **t** and **ss** can be turned into nouns by adding **ion**; e.g., act → act**ion**, discuss → discus**sion**.
> Sometimes we add the suffix **ation** because it is easier to say; e.g., inform → inform**ation**.
> If the verb ends in **e**, **drop the e** before adding **ion** or **ation**; e.g., create → creat**ion**, inspire → inspir**ation**.

List **①** **Write the word.**

action _____

discussion _____

direction _____

creation _____

connection _____

protection _____

location _____

prediction _____

election _____

collection _____

inspection _____

alteration _____

selection _____

temptation _____

translation _____

confession _____

prevention _____

limitation _____

confusion _____

education _____

② **Syllables.** Rearrange the syllables to make a list word.

a ect ion coll _____

b ion fess con _____

c it lim ion at _____

d ven tion pre _____

e ion fus con _____

f spec tion in _____

③ **Unscramble these list words.**

a caontiedu _____

b mptttaione _____

c noitaretla _____

d noitceles _____

e spectionin _____

f cteleion _____

g reatcion _____

h tinoac _____

i tantrslaion _____

④ **Complete the table.**

act	action
collect	
confuse	
educate	
select	
direct	
create	

Suffixes: ion, ation

1 Revise your spelling list from page 144. Complete each sentence with a list word.

a We used a map to find the _____ of the nearest hotel.

b The _____ to eat the cake was too great, so I cut myself a big slice.

c We had a heated _____ about which movie to watch.

d Tennille wears a helmet for _____ when she goes bike riding.

e My uncle is standing for Congress in the next _____ .

f We had gone in the wrong _____ and had to turn back.

g This is an English _____ of an Italian book.

Challenge words

2 Write the word.

congratulation _____

determination _____

information _____

imagination _____

expression _____

possession _____

exaggeration _____

communication _____

illustration _____

abbreviation _____

3 Word clues. Which challenge word means?

a drawing in a book _____

b an overstatement _____

c facts or knowledge _____

d makes you keep trying

_____

e shortened words _____

f owning something _____

g showing thoughts or feelings

_____

h images formed in the mind

_____

4 Complete the sentence.

a He told me he held his breath for 7 minutes, but I knew it was an _____.

b I'm collecting _____ about reptile species.

c It was her _____ that made her the great athlete she is today.

d Dad told me the monster was a product of my _____.

e My grandparents sent me a letter of _____ when I won the swimming championship.

Commas in compound sentences

A **compound sentence** contains two main clauses, each of which can stand on its own. The **clauses** are often joined with a conjunction; e.g., Meg hid behind the tree, **but** Emily soon found her. Usually there is a comma before the conjunction.

1 **Complete the sentences with a conjunction from the box.**

a He broke the clock, _____ he had to buy a new one.

b I bought the book last month, _____ I haven't read it yet.

c You can wear your red jacket, _____ you can wear the blue one.

d First we peeled the vegetables, _____ then we boiled them.

and
but
or
so

2 **Fill in commas before the conjunctions.**

a The door was open so we went inside.

b Tom hit the ball hard but Marcus caught it.

c The children were cold so they went inside.

d My bird is sick so tomorrow I will take her to the vet.

e We can eat at home or we can try the new restaurant.

f Amelia has tidied her room but she is jumping on the bed.

g I have made my mother a card and I have bought her a present.

3 **In the following pairs, check (✔) the sentence that needs a comma before the conjunction.**

a I bought eggs at the supermarket and bread at the bakery. ☐

b I bought the eggs at the supermarket and I got the bread at the bakery. ☐

c You can give it to me tomorrow or you can wait until the day after. ☐

d You can give it to me tomorrow or the day after. ☐

e I like chocolate ice cream but not vanilla. ☐

f I like chocolate ice cream but I don't like vanilla. ☐

L.4.2.C Use a comma before a coordinating conjunction in a compound sentence.

Spelling

Use this review to test your knowledge. It has three parts—**Spelling**, **Grammar**, and **Comprehension**. If you're unsure of an answer, go back and read the rules and generalizations in the blue boxes.

You have learned about:

- past tense
- vowel sound y
- suffix: ous
- endings: or, ure
- digraph: ch
- prefixes: in, im, ir, il
- digraphs: wh, ph, gh
- endings: in, ine, ain
- suffixes: ion, ation

1 **In each sentence, the spelling error has been <u>underlined</u>.** Write the correct spelling. 3 marks

  a "You've got a <u>fractor</u> in your foot," explained the doctor.   _____

  b It is a great <u>honure</u> to represent your country at the Olympics.   _____

  c On the cruise we saw whales, <u>dolphines</u>, and sharks.   _____

  d Denali in Alaska is the highest <u>mountine</u> peak of North America.   _____

  e It's hard to <u>imagin</u> a time before telephones.   _____

  f The <u>shef</u> created the most magnificent dessert.   _____

2 **Which word correctly completes this sentence?** 1 mark

Our Thanksgiving turkey was absolutely _____.

  a delicious   b delight   c treat   d enjoy

3 **This sentence has one word that is incorrect. Write the correct spelling.** 1 mark

Our local library has an excellent selection of comic books.   _____

4 **Complete these words with the sounds wh, ph, or gh.** 1 mark

  a ___ ___rase   b spa ___ ___ etti   c ___ ___isk   d hy ___ ___ en

5 **Circle the correct verb to complete each sentence.** 2 marks

  a I (weep, weeping, wept) when I fell off my skateboard.

  b I'd never (ride, riding, ridden) in a trolley car until we visited San Francisco.

6 **Complete each word with the correct prefix (in, im, ir, il).** 1 mark

  a ___ ___ polite   b ___ ___ legal   c ___ ___ accurate   d ___ ___ regular

7 **This sentence has one word that is incorrect. Write the correct spelling.** 1 mark

This year I am going to get a new bicicle with a basket for flowers.

Your score

_____

10

Grammar

You have learned about:

- punctuating dialogue
- reported speech
- run-on sentences
- frequently confused words
- modal auxiliaries
- simple and compound sentences
- punctuating quotations
- subjects and predicates
- punctuating compound sentences

1 **In the following sentences, fill in the missing punctuation.** 2 marks

    a "Let's go for a swim said Andy.

    b Marty said Please put the milk back in the fridge

2 **Circle the correct words in parentheses to complete each sentence.** 3 marks

    a I told them to put (there, their) bags over (there, their).

    b (Were, Where) are the keys that (were, where) on the table?

    c Come over (here, hear) so I can (here, hear) what you're saying.

3 **Fill in the quotation marks in the following sentences.** 2 marks

    a How quickly can you say She sells seashells on the seashore?

    b On the front of the card it said Happy birthday!

4 **Complete the second sentence in each pair.** 2 marks

    a "I have never been to California," said Maxine.

    Maxine said that _____

    _____

    b "Do you have a dog?" asked Will.

    Will asked me if _____

5 **Use the information in italics to help you choose the correct verb in parentheses.**
Color the answer. 4 marks

    a We (will, might) go to the beach.   *It is a possibility.*

    b I (will, might) visit my friends later.   *It is certain to happen.*

    c You (should, must) go home now.   *It is necessary that you go home.*

    d Alex (can, may) win that race.   *Alex is able to do it.*

Grammar

6 In each sentence, color the subject and underline the predicate. 2 marks

   a The yellow butterfly has landed on that flower.

   b My parents are taking me to Mount Rushmore.

7 Write the run-on sentences below correctly. 2 marks

   a I love basketball, I would play every day if I could. _____

   _____

   b I left the keys on the table, someone must have taken them. _____

   _____

8 Join each pair of sentences with one of these conjunctions: *and, but, so.* Use the correct punctuation. 3 marks

   a It started to rain. I put up my umbrella. _____

   _____

   b I looked everywhere for my book. I couldn't find it. _____

   _____

   c I put my socks in the drawer. I put my shirt in the cupboard. _____

   _____

Your score

☐

20

149

The Crow

Read the passage and then use the comprehension skills you have learned to answer the questions.

Kelly is a black crow with a sharp beak and shiny feathers. He lives in a scraggly nest in a hollow tree, right in the middle of Farmer Flynn's farm. From his home high up in the tree, he can see the mountains in the distance and the river flowing away to the west.

But today Kelly isn't interested in the mountains or the river. He is watching Farmer Flynn plow the field, turning over the rich, black soil in long, straight furrows. When the farmer passes by, Kelly swoops down low over the furrows.

"What a feast I'll have today," he thinks. He follows Farmer Flynn on his tractor and pecks at the juicy grubs that the plow turn up. How fresh and tasty they are!

After he has eaten his fill, Kelly flies back to his tree to snooze in the warm afternoon sun. When he wakens, the sun is low in the west. Kelly remembers the delicious meal he ate earlier and looks down at the newly-plowed ground. He blinks when he sees something shining in the furrow. Curious, he flies down and lands nearby, then sidles cautiously towards the object. He gives it a peck. He jumps back in fright as it begins to make a noise— *tick, tick, tick, tick.*

Kelly stares at the yellow object for a long time. Then he pecks at it again ... and again. He shakes it in his beak. Suddenly the yellow thing wraps itself around his leg. Now Kelly is really frightened! He flies back to his tree with the yellow, ticking thing hanging from one leg.

Kelly perches on a branch and pecks at his enemy again and again. Eventually it loosens its grip on his leg and falls down into the hollow of his tree. He can still hear it ticking, but he is free at last. Kelly flies around his tree, squawking triumphantly.

Many months later, Farmer Flynn is mowing the grass near Kelly's tree. He stops to have lunch in its cool shade. As he is eating, he notices something shining in the hollow of the tree. He reaches in and pulls out a gold chain.

"Stars and bananas!" he exclaims. "It's my old pocket watch. Now how did it get here?"

The Crow

1 Where is Kelly's nest? 1 mark   **LITERAL**

   a in a tree on a mountain   **b** in a tree on a farm

   c in a tree beside the river   **d** in a tree in the city

2 Why would Farmer Flynn be plowing the field? 1 mark   **CRITICAL**

   a to make it look neater   **b** to destroy the grubs

   c to get rid of the weeds   **d** to prepare it for planting

3 Which word in the text is similar in meaning to 'sleep'? 1 mark   **VOCABULARY**

   a blinks   **b** swoops   **c** snooze   **d** wakens

4 The pocket watch is described as being shiny and yellow. This suggests
that it is made of ... 1 mark   **INFERENTIAL**

   a silver.   **b** stainless steel.   **c** gold.   **d** plastic.

5 Why is Kelly frightened of the pocket watch? Choose the TWO best answers. 1 mark   **CRITICAL**

   a It is a strange shape.   **b** It is shiny and yellow.

   c It makes a strange noise.   **d** It wraps itself around his leg.

6 Give a text clue to support your answer to question 5. 2 marks   **CRITICAL**

_____

_____

_____

7 Which words best describe Farmer Flynn's feelings when he finds his
pocket watch? 1 mark   **INFERENTIAL**

   a surprised and puzzled   **b** surprised and annoyed

   c disappointed and confused   **d** curious and worried

8 What is the most likely reason Farmer Flynn's pocket watch was in the furrow
in the first place? 2 marks   **CRITICAL**

Your
score

[ ]

10

_____

_____

Your Review 3 Scores

Spelling		Grammar		Comprehension		Total
[ ]	+	[ ]	+	[ ]	=	[ ]
10		**20**		**10**		**40**

On Our Way to Alpha Centauri

Making connections
Linking a text to events in your own life is a great way to build understanding. Look for key words and phrases in the text to make the connections.

Read the passage.

Underline the words that describe Sarah's new home.

Put a box around the word that refers to the time ahead.

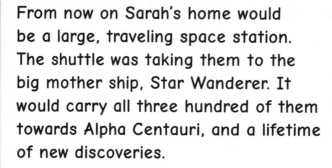

From now on Sarah's home would be a large, traveling space station. The shuttle was taking them to the big mother ship, Star Wanderer. It would carry all three hundred of them towards Alpha Centauri, and a lifetime of new discoveries.

Suddenly Sarah was scared. It was such an unknown future that lay ahead—like it was for those sailors, hundreds of years ago, sailing over the edge of the Earth.

Circle the correct answer/s for each question.

1 Which of the following have you experienced?
  a living on a space station
  b moving to another home
  c making new discoveries
  d traveling on a space shuttle
  e feeling scared
  f sailing on the ocean
  g wondering what the future holds
  h traveling somewhere with lots of other people

2 Which of the following is it possible you will experience in the future?
  a embark on exciting adventures   b sail over the edge of a flat Earth
  c travel in outer space   d sail around the world

On Our Way to Alpha Centauri

Read the
whole story

On Our Way to
Alpha Centauri

Read the passage.

Underline a sentence that suggests that the people celebrating Christmas are not on Earth.

Circle the object that Sarah considers to be the most important part of Christmas.

"We've all left a lot behind us," started Sarah, and many faces grew serious. Dr. Singh was worried. Was Sarah going to remind them too much of earthly celebrations?

"For me, the most important part of Christmas is the Christmas tree. Every year I'd dream about what it would look like. I couldn't wait until it was time to start decorating it." Sarah continued, "Kapil and I have something special that comes from Earth. Something from the past to take us into the future."

Sarah signalled to Kapil, who tugged a cord.

The curtain fell. In front of them was a young apple tree, holding its branches and green leaves high. Seven red apples hung from the branches.

Highlight who helped Sarah prepare the Christmas surprise.

Color the phrase that describes the tree.

Sarah, Kapil, and the other people on the spaceship are celebrating their first Christmas away from Earth.

1 Write a paragraph describing a celebration, such as your birthday, Halloween, or a religious holiday, that you have especially enjoyed. What did you do? What did you eat? Were there decorations? Did you receive presents? Which of your friends or family members shared the celebration with you?

_____

_____

_____

_____

_____

_____

_____

_____

RL.4.1 Refer to details and examples in a text when explaining what the text says explicitly and when drawing inferences from the text.

Prefixes: re, de, pre

The **prefix re** can mean **to go back** or **to do again**; e.g., do → **re**do.

The **prefix de** means **to remove**; e.g., mystify → **de**mystify.

The **prefix pre** means **before**; e.g., date → **pre**date.

List

1 **Write the word.**

decode _____

redo _____

rearrange _____

prepack _____

redirect _____

replay _____

regroup _____

prepay _____

prewash _____

reboot _____

readjust _____

premature _____

debrief _____

debone _____

rephrase _____

prehistory _____

delouse _____

reroute _____

reappoint _____

defuse _____

2 **Chunks.** Rearrange the chunks to make a list word.

a   oup gr re   _____

b   wa pre sh   _____

c   just re ad   _____

d   ck pa pre   _____

e   app re oint   _____

f   st pre ory hi   _____

g   is re sue   _____

h   lou de se   _____

i   ma pre tu re   _____

3 **Word clues.** Which list word means?

a   to watch again   _____

b   give money in advance   _____

c   to remove lice   _____

d   happens too soon   _____

e   to do again   _____

f   to remove bones   _____

g   before written history   _____

h   to remove the danger   _____

4 **Sort the words.**

re		de	pre

L.4.2.D Spell grade-appropriate words correctly.

Prefixes: re, de, pre

1 **Revise your spelling list from page 154.** Underline the spelling mistakes. Write the word correctly.

a We had to deacode the ancient hieroglyphs. _____

b They will debreef the astronauts when they return. _____

c The police tried to defuze the situation. _____

d I spent all day trying to reearange my bedroom. _____

e Mom asked the butcher to deebone the meat. _____

f I had to redoe my washing after it rained. _____

g I decided to prepaye my ticket to save time. _____

h I had to refrase my answer so that they understood. _____

Challenge words

2 **Write the word.**

regain _____

preshrink _____

demystify _____

reupholster _____

repopulate _____

preknowledge _____

reissue _____

demotivate _____

rebroadcast _____

reassemble _____

3 **Complete the sentence.**

a Scientists are trying to _____ the area with native plants and animals.

b Dad wants to _____ his old chair.

c The basketball team tried to _____ their lead in the second half.

d My favorite program is going to be _____ this weekend.

e The scientist is going to _____ the information by explaining it in a simple way.

4 **Another way to say it.** Which challenge word could replace the underlined word?

a After being sick, I am starting to <u>recover</u> my strength. _____

b I can't wait for the <u>reprint</u> of my favorite book. _____

c We have decided to <u>recover</u> our comfortable old sofa. _____

d The crowd started to <u>reunite</u> outside city hall after the parade. _____

Subordinate clauses

A **clause** is a group of words that contains a **verb**. A **main clause** makes sense by itself. A **subordinate clause** does not make sense by itself; e.g., I went to the party (main clause) because she invited me (subordinate clause). Many subordinate clauses start with a **conjunction** like although, because, until, when, and while.

1 **Check (✔) the subordinate clauses.**

a while I was waiting ☐   b when they arrived ☐

c I waited at the bus stop ☐   d he is getting impatient ☐

e she is waiting over there ☐   f because she took a long time ☐

g although I was waiting for him ☐   h I told them to wait for me ☐

i whenever I have to wait ☐   j since I last saw her ☐

k I will see you later ☐   l until their plane arrives ☐

2 **Match the clause to the picture.**

a

b

c

_____   _____   _____

because it's delicious   before the rain starts   if the shoes fit

3 **Complete each sentence with a word from the box.**

a _____ you eat too much chocolate, you will be sick.

b _____ the car is small, it is very spacious inside.

c He wouldn't eat the orange _____ it was sour.

d I held onto the rope _____ they said I could let go.

e We bumped into our friends _____ we were in Boston.

f You can have the last piece of pie, _____ someone else wants it.

although
until
if
when
unless
because

L.4.1 Demonstrate command of the conventions of standard English grammar and usage when writing or speaking.

Lure

Making inferences
Use clues in the text to make inferences (form opinions). The clues will help you find the answers that are hiding in the text.

Read the passage.

Circle the adjective the narrator uses to describe the kind of fisherkid she is.

Underline the sentence that shows that the narrator likes to spend her free time fishing.

I must be the worst fisherkid on Earth!

It isn't that I don't try. Every chance I get, I'm dangling a line in the water somewhere. My bookshelves are full of every fishing book and fishing map ever printed. I buy the best fishing line pocket money can buy. And I watch all the fishing reports on TV and listen to them on the radio as well.

Highlight two sentences that suggest the narrator knows a lot about fishing.

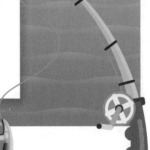

Circle the correct answer for each question.

1 What can we **infer** about the narrator?
   a   She hates fishing.
   c   She loves fishing.
   b   She likes eating fish.
   d   She wants to give fishing a try.

2 Which sentence is the best **clue** to question 1's answers?
   a   Every chance I get, I'm dangling a line in the water somewhere.
   b   I must be the worst fisherkid on Earth!
   c   It isn't that I don't try.
   d   I buy the best fishing line pocket money can buy.

3 What can we **infer** about the number of fish the narrator catches?
   a   She always catches lots of fish.
   c   She never catches any fish.
   b   She sometimes catches lots of fish.
   d   She often catches a few fish.

4 Which sentence is the best **clue** to question 3's answer?
   a   Every chance I get, I'm dangling a line in the water somewhere.
   b   It isn't that I don't try.
   c   I buy the best fishing line pocket money can buy.
   d   I must be the worst fisherkid on Earth!

Read the **whole story**

Lure

Lure

Read the passage.

<u>Underline</u> the words that describe the place where the fishermen went missing.

Color the name of the place where the men went missing.

The fishing report suddenly becomes very serious. The reporter is warning people about the dangers of fishing from a popular local spot. Two fishermen have gone missing. The camera zooms in on the spot where the fishermen were last seen.

I know the spot—it's called Devil's Rocks. It's a good spot to catch kingfish. Suddenly, a huge wave comes out of nowhere and crashes over the rocky ledge.

Highlight words that show that the narrator is watching television.

Put a box around the words that suggest that Devil's Rocks is near the ocean.

1 We can **infer** that people often visit the spot where the two fishermen went missing. What is the **clue**?

_____

_____

2 The reporter warns that it could be dangerous to fish from the spot where the two men went missing. What other **clue** is there to **suggest** that this is a dangerous spot?

_____

_____

3 We can **infer** that the narrator is watching the fishing report on television. What are the **clues**?

_____

_____

4 What **evidence** is there to **suggest** that the spot where the men were fishing is near the ocean?

_____

_____

RL.4.1 Refer to details and examples in a text when explaining what the text says explicitly and when drawing inferences from the text.

Suffixes: ment, ship, hood, dom

Many verbs can be turned into nouns by adding the suffix **ment**; e.g., entertain → entertain**ment**.

Some words can be turned into abstract nouns by adding the suffixes **ship**, **hood**, or **dom**; e.g., friend → friend**ship**, knight → knight**hood**, free → free**dom**.

List   ① **Write the word.**

agreement _____

hardship _____

wisdom _____

kingdom _____

friendship _____

freedom _____

treatment _____

childhood _____

statement _____

enjoyment _____

leadership _____

movement _____

retirement _____

adulthood _____

argument _____

boredom _____

excitement _____

membership _____

brotherhood _____

relationship _____

② **Unscramble these list words.**

a   rbdmoeo _____

b   tseametnt _____

c   doborhehtro _____

d   olhaodtud _____

e   dlciohdoh _____

f   emaengert _____

g   hasleripde _____

h   hsairpdh _____

i   metirerent _____

③ **Word clues.** Which list word means?

a   ruled by a king or queen

_____

b   nothing interesting to do

_____

c   to be at liberty _____

d   when you are young _____

e   a verbal disagreement _____

④ **Missing suffix.** Rewrite the word with the correct suffix.

agree	agreement
excite	
brother	
leader	
child	
enjoy	
king	
wise	

Suffixes: ment, ship, hood, dom

1 Revise your spelling list from page 159. Complete each sentence with a list word.

a When we won the championship, we felt great _____.

b If you are not imprisoned you have _____.

c Something that isn't still is in a state of _____.

d When people disagree they could have an _____.

e If you like doing something it brings you _____.

f If you say something you make a _____.

g A king rules his _____.

Challenge words

2 Write the word.

improvement _____

kinship _____

livelihood _____

arrangement _____

announcement _____

development _____

entertainment _____

championship _____

equipment _____

government _____

3 Word clues. Which challenge word means?

a gear or apparatus _____

b political control _____

c make better _____

d public statement _____

e providing amusement _____

f a contest _____

g a way of earning money _____

h placed in a particular order _____

4 Complete each sentence.

a My coach told me he had noticed a great _____ in my ability.

b We all gathered to hear the President's _____.

c Our team actually has a shot at winning the _____ this year.

d I was not happy with the _____ of my room.

e TV, games, and movies are all forms of _____.

f I am saving my pocket money so I can buy some new sports _____.

L.4.2.D Spell grade-appropriate words correctly.

Relative pronouns

The most common **relative pronouns** are **who**, **whose**, **which**, and **that**. They introduce a **subordinate clause**; e.g., I spoke to the boy **who** won the trophy. The girl, **whose** bag this is, is in Wilson's chess club.

1 **Complete each sentence with a relative pronoun.**

a My brother, _____ is ten, is a Boy Scout.

b I want a kitten _____ has a cute face and a fluffy tail.

c The spider, _____ was big and hairy, was in my cupboard.

d The girl _____ crayons I borrowed wants them back.

e That is the man _____ fixed my bicycle.

f I took the book _____ no-one else wanted.

2 **In each sentence, circle the relative pronoun and underline the noun it refers to.**

a The boys, who are best friends, are going hiking together.

b The cake, which was delicious, came from our local bakery.

c I have finished the sandwiches that were in the picnic basket.

d I was talking to the boy whose parents come from Africa.

3 **Match the clauses. Underline the relative pronouns.**

Main clause	**Subordinate clause**
a I haven't seen the movie	which was the best present I'd ever had.
b That's the pilot	whose mother was in hospital.
c My parents gave me a bike,	who will fly the plane.
d I sympathized with the girl	that you are talking about.

4 **Complete each sentence.**

a The people who _____

_____

b The man whose _____

_____

Wilderness-wacked

Descriptive verbs help us visualize the actions in a text. To identify the descriptive verbs, look for verbs that tell exactly how an action is performed; e.g., 'raced' instead of 'ran.'

Read the passage.

Circle the verb that is similar in meaning to stood up.

Highlight the verb that creates a picture of someone moving slowly and carefully.

Leaving the brilliant sunshine, it took a while for his eyes to adjust to the inky blackness. The hairs on the back of his neck bristled. Unaware that he was holding his breath, Spook inched forward, his shoes scraping on the earth. His fists were clenched. His fingernails bit into his palms.

The cave was narrow inside. Cobwebs veiled the walls like gauze.

Put a box around the verb that creates a picture of a creature sinking its teeth into flesh.

Underline the verb that creates a picture of something soft and filmy.

Circle the correct answer for each question.

1 Which **verb** in the passage is similar in meaning to moved?

  a bristled   b scraping   c inched   d clenched

2 Why is the **verb** you chose in question 1 more effective than "moved"? It creates a picture of how ...

  a awkwardly Spook moved.   b slowly and carefully Spook moved.

  c quickly Spook moved.   d smoothly and gracefully Spook moved.

3 Which of the following words from the text is **not a descriptive verb**?

  a clenched   b bit   c bristled   d was

4 Which **verb** in the passage is similar in meaning to "covered"?

  a veiled   b bristled   c clenched   d was holding

5 Why is the **verb** you chose in question 4 more effective than covered? It creates a picture of how ...

  a thick and rough the cobwebs were.   b thin and delicate the cobwebs were.

  c sticky and dirty the cobwebs were.   d messy word broken the cobwebs were.

Wilderness-wacked

Read the whole story

Read the passage.

Circle the verb that is similar in meaning to ran.

Highlight the verbs that suggest that the branches and thorns were attacking the boys.

Feet barely contacting the ground, the boys bolted—chased by the scream. Spook was in the lead, then Nathan and, well behind, Aaron, his short legs hardly able to keep pace. Branches and thorns stabbed and snatched at them. Long grass tickled their legs like creepy crawlies.

Eventually, out of breath, the trio stopped. They doubled over and gasped for air and their legs ached.

Color the verb that lets us imagine what the grass felt like on the boys' legs.

Underline the verb that shows that the boys were taking short, quick breaths.

1 Which **descriptive verb** has the author used in place of "ran"?

_____

2 What **picture** of the thorns do the **verbs** "stabbed" and "snatched" create?

_____

_____

3 The author writes that the long grass tickled the boys' legs. What **picture** does the **verb** "tickled" create?

_____

_____

_____

4 What does the **verb** "gasped" **suggest** about the way the boys were breathing?

_____

_____

Endings: ery, ary, ory

> Many words that end in **ery**, **ary**, and **ory** have a similar end sound; e.g. cutlery, glossary, ivory.

List **① Write the word.**

celery _____

cutlery _____

ivory _____

February _____

primary _____

history _____

machinery _____

fishery _____

robbery _____

pottery _____

slavery _____

voluntary _____

secondary _____

boundary _____

artery _____

glossary _____

surgery _____

directory _____

scenery _____

salary _____

② Chunks. Rearrange the chunks to make a list word.

a er fi y sh _____

b ry sal a _____

c y vol tar un _____

d er y slav _____

e ect y dir or _____

f vor y i _____

g oss ary gl _____

h ler y cut _____

i y ter pot _____

③ Word clues. Which list word means?

a a vegetable _____

b money a person makes _____

c things made of clay _____

d the second month _____

e stealing _____

f used to eat with _____

g an operation _____

④ Underline the spelling mistakes. Write the word correctly.

a The police arrived at the scene of the robary very quickly. _____

b They were told not to cross the boundory. _____

c Mixing two primary colors makes a secondery color. _____

d I gave my rabbit some cellery to munch on. _____

e I went to the library to research the town's hestory. _____

f We gazed at the seenery from the top of the mountain. _____

g My weekend was filled with volentery work. _____

Endings: ery, ary, ory

1 **Revise your spelling list from page 164.** Fill in the missing list word.

a _____ is the second month of the year.

b I went to set the table for dinner but couldn't find the _____.

c I looked up the unknown word in the _____ of my book.

d An elephant's tusks are made of _____.

e The heart pumps blood out through one main _____.

f The nurses prepared the patient for _____.

g I bought clay for my _____ class.

Challenge words

2 **Write the word.**

finery _____

treachery _____

embroidery _____

observatory _____

customary _____

anniversary _____

satisfactory _____

temporary _____

extraordinary _____

confectionary _____

3 **Word clues.** Which challenge word means?

a sewing _____

b celebrated each year

_____

c not permanent _____

d candies _____

e incredible _____

f expensive clothes _____

g tradition, usual _____

h where you watch the stars

_____

4 **Complete each sentence.**

a My brother's _____ broke my father's heart.

b The _____ around the hem is starting to come undone.

c We went to the _____ to watch the meteor shower.

d Today is my grandparents' 60th wedding _____.

e It is _____ to thank people for their gifts.

f We had to move into _____ accomodation while our house was being renovated.

Relative adverbs

The most common **relative adverbs** are **where**, **when**, and **why**. They introduce a subordinate clause; e.g., That is the park **where** we like to play. That was the day **when** my grandparents arrived. That is (the reason) **why** I'm not playing today.

1 **Complete each sentence with *where, when,* or *why*.**

a We have just passed the house _____ my best friend lives.

b We asked the little boy _____ he was crying.

c That was the year _____ my sister was born.

d That is the restaurant _____ we had dinner last night.

e My parents asked me _____ the team had done so badly.

f I remember the time _____ the river burst its banks.

2 **In each sentence, circle the relative adverb and underline the noun it refers to.**

a My friend visited the town where my cousins live.

b I can guess the reason why he is so happy.

c It happened on a night when nobody was at home.

d I found the place where I'd left my hat.

e There was a time when woolly mammoths roamed the earth.

3 **Complete each sentence.**

a We searched the room where _____

_____

b I know the reason why _____

_____

c Twelve o'clock is the hour when _____

_____

d The children went to the beach where _____

_____

L.4.1.A Use relative adverbs.

The Eagle and the Spider

Compare and contrast
Compare and contrast by looking for the similarities and differences between details in the text.

Read the passage.

Circle the clue to how Eagle reached the top of the mountain.

Highlight how Spider moved above Eagle's head.

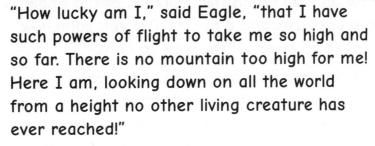

"How lucky am I," said Eagle, "that I have such powers of flight to take me so high and so far. There is no mountain too high for me! Here I am, looking down on all the world from a height no other living creature has ever reached!"

"What a boaster you are," said Spider, from a nearby twig. "Look where I am sitting. It isn't so far below you, is it?" Spider jumped to another twig, just above Eagle's head. He began to busily spin a web, just above Eagle.

"How did you reach this height?" asked Eagle. "You are weak and wingless. Did you somehow manage to crawl all the way up here?"

Underline what Spider did when he was above Eagle's head.

Put a box around how Eagle thought Spider had reached the top of the mountain.

Circle the correct answer for each question.

1 In what way are Eagle and Spider **similar**? Both are ...
   a birds.
   b animals.
   c insects.
   d mammals.

2 In what way are Eagle and Spider **different**? Only ...
   a Spider can fly.
   b Spider can hop.
   c Eagle can fly.
   d Eagle can run.

3 What can Spider do that Eagle can't?
   a spin a web
   b flap its wings
   c build a nest
   d soar above the earth

4 Which of the following sentences is **true**?
   a Spider is bigger than Eagle.
   b Spider is stronger than Eagle.
   c Eagle is shorter than Spider.
   d Eagle is heavier than Spider.

The Eagle and the Spider

Read the passage.

Underline the reason Eagle was surprised that Spider had reached the top of the mountain.

Highlight the clue to how the wind affected Eagle.

Color words that tell how Spider reached the top of the mountain.

Underline the words that tell what the wind did to Spider.

"How did you reach this height?" asked Eagle. "You are weak and wingless. Did you somehow manage to crawl all the way up here?"

"No!" laughed Spider. "I simply attached myself to you, and you lifted me from the valleys below on your tail feathers. And I can get along very well without your help too, now that I am way up here. So, Eagle, don't put on any airs with me, because I want to tell you that ..."

Suddenly, a gust of wind swept across the top of the mountain. It slid right by Eagle but it brushed Spider, web and all, back down into the depths of the valley.

1. Carefully explain **the different ways** in which Eagle and Spider reached the top of the mountain.

_____

_____

_____

_____

2. **Why** didn't the wind blow Eagle off the mountain?

_____

_____

3. **Why** did the wind blow Spider off the mountain?

_____

Suffixes: able, ible

Adding the suffix **able** to a word turns it into an adjective; e.g., reason → reason**able**.

If the base word ends in **e**, **drop the e** before adding **able**; e.g., ador**e** → ador**able**.

If the base word **ends in y** and there is a <u>consonant before</u> the **y**, change the **y** to **i** before adding **able**; e.g., rel**y** → rel**i**able.

Some adjectives take the suffix **ible**; e.g., flex**ible**. Many of these words have Latin or Greek origins.

List   **1** **Write the word.**

suitable _____

bearable _____

visible _____

edible _____

flexible _____

enjoyable _____

affordable _____

favorable _____

terrible _____

comfortable _____

predictable _____

reasonable _____

sensible _____

adjustable _____

valuable _____

acceptable _____

fashionable _____

reliable _____

respectable _____

advisable _____

2 **Chunks.** Rearrange the chunks to make a list word.

a ta dic ble pre _____

b vi ad sa ble _____

c for ta ble com _____

d ta spec ble re _____

e a joy ble en _____

f jus ble ta ad _____

g da ble aff or _____

3 **Missing letters.** Write the missing letters.

a suit_____   b afford_____

c sens_____   d adjust_____

e bear_____   f terr_____

g valu_____   h adjust_____

i reli_____   j enjoy_____

k accept_____   l favor_____

m fashion_____   n reason_____

4 **Meaning.** Which list word means?

a Right or appropriate for a particular situation or purpose _____

b Can be bigger or smaller _____

c Following a style that is popular _____

d Capable of being trusted; dependable _____

e Having good judgment _____

f Able to tell in advance that an event will happen _____

Suffixes: able, ible

1 **Revise your spelling list from page 169.** Complete the sentence.

a Amy is _____ and looks both ways before crossing the road.

b My new deluxe armchair is very _____.

c We were asked to wear _____ clothing for the wet weather.

d The gymnast was very _____.

e We had an _____ day at the beach.

f There was a _____ storm last night that ripped out several trees.

g The judge decided on _____ punishment.

Challenge words

2 **Write the word.**

manageable _____

divisible _____

imaginable _____

accessible _____

avoidable _____

believable _____

reversible _____

questionable _____

noticeable _____

admirable _____

3 **Hidden words.** Find the challenge word.

a sdfsdimaginableg _____

b fvdfsbelievabledfs _____

c vdgvsadmirablefg _____

d sdfvnoticeabledf _____

e okpmanageableo _____

f ajhndivisiblefsdfv _____

g sfdbiavoidablegvr _____

h dgfrgreversiblefg _____

4 **Complete each sentence.**

a My _____ dress had flowers on one side and stripes on the other.

b The actor in the play was not very _____.

c The store built wheelchair ramps so getting around was _____ for everyone.

d The new candy shop had every single chocolate bar _____.

e The scar on his arm was quite _____.

Relative clauses

A **relative clause** is a type of **subordinate clause**. It gives information about **nouns** and **pronouns**. Relative clauses are introduced by:
- the **relative pronouns** **who**, **whose**, **which**, or **that**; e.g., Our **cousins**, **who** live in Los Angeles, are coming to visit us.
- the **relative adverbs** **where**, **when**, or **why**; e.g., Los Angeles is the **city** **where** our cousins live.

1 **In each sentence, state whether the underlined word is a relative pronoun, or a relative adverb.**

a   I don't know <u>why</u> she is angry with me.   _____

b   The student <u>who</u> finishes first will win a prize.   _____

c   I remember the day <u>when</u> I got my first bike.   _____

d   The movie, <u>which</u> I watched last week, is very good. _____

e   The boy <u>whose</u> scarf this is sits over there.   _____

f   That is the beach <u>where</u> you'll find the best shells. _____

2 **In each sentence, underline the relative clause. Hint! It starts with a relative pronoun or adverb.**

a   That is the house where the famous actor lives.

b   I think I know the reason why the lights are flickering.

c   The mayor is talking to the boys who broke the window.

d   I will lend you the book that I bought online.

e   Yesterday was one of those days when everything went wrong.

f   The books, which have leather covers, are very old.

3 **Complete each sentence.**

a   I met him at the shop where _____

   _____

b   The President presented the prize to the athlete who _____

   _____

c   They towed away the car that _____

   _____

Engineering Feats

Read the passage.

Circle the name of the river on which Hoover Dam is built.

Highlight the year in which work on Hoover Dam began.

Color the year in which Hoover Dam was completed.

Hoover Dam controls the flow of the Colorado River. It is on the border between the states of Arizona and Nevada.

Work on the dam began in 1931. Men poured concrete 24 hours a day, seven days a week. The dam was completed in 1935, more than two years ahead of schedule.

Hoover Dam allowed more people to live in America's southwest. The reliable water supply is used for farming. Electricity from the dam's power station is used by people in three states.

Underline the states that Hoover Dam borders.

Put a box around one of the things the water supply from Hoover Dam is used for.

Circle the correct answers for each question.

1 **Where** is Hoover Dam? On the border between ...
- a Arkansas and Nevada
- b Arizona and New Mexico
- c Arizona and Nebraska
- d Arizona and Nevada

2 On **which** river is Hoover Dam? On the ...
- a Arizona River
- b Mississippi River
- c Colorado River
- d Snake River

3 **When** was the dam completed?
- a in 1931
- b in 1935
- c in 1924
- d in 1937

4 **How** many years ahead of schedule was the dam completed?
- a less than two
- b exactly two
- c more than two
- d three

5 In **what** part of the United States is Hoover Dam? In the ...
- a southwest
- b west
- c northwest
- d south

  RI.4.1 Refer to details and examples in a text when explaining what the text says explicitly and when drawing inferences from the text.

Engineering Feats

Read the full text

Engineering Feats

Read the passage.

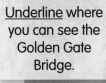

Underline where you can see the Golden Gate Bridge.

Highlight what kind of bridge the Golden Gate Bridge is.

The Golden Gate Bridge is a suspension bridge across the opening of San Francisco Bay.

Many people said a bridge could not be built there. There are strong currents in the bay, and the water is up to 330 feet deep. It is also a very windy and foggy site.

The Golden Gate was the longest suspension bridge in the world when it was completed in 1937. The bridge's two main cables connect to each end of the bridge and hold up the road. Each one is made of more than 27,000 thinner cables.

Put a box around how deep the bay is.

Circle the date the Golden Gate Bridge was completed.

32 USA
Golden Gate Bridge

1 **Where** is the Golden Gate Bridge?

_____

2 **What** kind of bridge is the Golden Gate Bridge?

_____

3 **How** deep is the water in the bay?

_____

4 **When** was the Golden Gate Bridge completed?

_____

5 **What** holds up the road?

_____

Latin origins

Many English words come from Latin words; e.g., **terra** means *earth* in Latin and from terra we get **terr**ain, **terr**itory, and **terr**estrial.

List **1** **Write the word.**

scribe
script
scribble
describe
decade
scale
audience
terrace
manual
December
prescribe
terrain
territory
manager
decimal
audition
manicure
annually
manually
prescription

2 **Name.**

a _____ b _____

3 **Unscramble these list words.**

a treiytorr _____
b nymalual _____
c becsri _____
d retarni _____
e mdicela _____
f enmaciru _____
g elbbircs _____
h rnpiorcetspi _____

4 **Meaning.** Which list word means?

a A group gathered to watch something
b A device used for measuring weight
c The natural characteristics of a section of land
d Ten years
e To write quickly and carelessly
f The twelfth month of the year
g A treatment for your fingernails

Latin origins

1 **Revise your spelling list from page 174.** Underline the mistakes.
Write the word correctly.

a He was trying to descrybe what his old house looked like. _____

b Descemba comes at the end of the year. _____

c We looked at the car manuel to see what could be wrong. _____

d We had to awdition for a role in the play. _____

e The awdiance cheered and clapped loudly. _____

f We weighed the flour on the kitchen scaile. _____

g She had drawn a scribel that looked like a cat. _____

h My mother is the mainager of a large store. _____

Challenge words

2 **Write the word.**

escalate _____

anniversary _____

decibel _____

manipulate _____

terrestrial _____

territorial _____

manufacture _____

manicurist _____

terrarium _____

subterranean _____

3 **Word clues.** Which challenge word means?

a relating to the earth _____

b a measure of sound _____

c to make something _____

d to increase _____

e used to grow plants in

_____

f a yearly celebration _____

g defending an area of land

_____

h below the earth's surface

_____

4 **Complete each sentence.**

a The explorers found a _____ cave filled with purple gem stones.

b I stayed silent because I did not want the argument to _____.

c Zoe was trying to _____ her clay into the shape of a cat.

d The factory can _____ 200 cars a day.

e Her voice rises a _____ when she is mad.

Questions and exclamations

A sentence that asks a question ends with a question mark (?);
e.g., **How** old are you? **What** are you doing?

Sentences or phrases that start with **How** or **What** can also end with
an **exclamation point** (!); e.g., **How** exciting! **What** an amazing day!
These usually express a strong feeling.

1 **End each phrase or sentence with a question mark or exclamation point.**

a   How did you get to school today

b   How fantastic

c   What a talented singer she is

d   What is that song called

e   How many people have you invited to your party

f   How amazing is that view

g   What a cute little dog

h   How many times have you been to the park

i   What did you eat for dinner

j   What a delicious meal that was

2 **Complete each sentence so that it asks a question.**

a   How _____

   _____

b   What _____

   _____

3 **Complete each sentence so that it needs an exclamation point at the end.**

a   How _____

   _____

b   What _____

   _____

L.4.1 Demonstrate command of the conventions of standard English grammar and usage when writing or speaking.

Oceans

Read the passages.

Plants are an essential part of the ocean's food chains. Some sea creatures eat plants. Others are carnivores that eat other sea creatures.

Food chains in the ocean begin with plankton. Plankton is a mixture of tiny animals and algae. Like all plants, the algae use the sun's energy to make food. Very small crustaceans feed on the tiny algae and together they are known as plankton.

Underline the words in each text that tell what plankton is.

Highlight the words in each text that tell how algae make food.

Color the words in each text that tell what tiny crustaceans feed on.

The word plankton is Greek for wanderer or drifter. It refers to a category of drifting organisms found in the middle and upper levels of the ocean.

Plankton consists of algae, which live near the surface where they can draw on the sun's energy to make food, and tiny crustaceans that feed on the algae.

Small creatures such as krill and shrimps feed on the plankton and larger fish eat the shrimps.

1 Which information appears in **both** texts?

a where the word plankton comes from

b what plankton consists of

c where algae live

d how algae make food

e what tiny crustaceans eat

f what krill and shrimps eat

g what larger fish eat

RI.4.9 Integrate information from two texts on the same topic in order to write or speak about the subject knowledgeably.

177

Oceans

Read the full text

Oceans

Read the passages.

The ocean floor has many of the same features you find on land. Mountain ranges, volcanoes, deep trenches, and wide, flat plains are all found on the ocean floor.

When measured from the ocean floor, Hawaii's Mauna Kea rises more than 30,000 feet, making it the tallest mountain on Earth!

Chains of underwater volcanoes, known as seamounts, exist on all ocean floors. Some islands are seamounts that have risen out of the ocean. The Hawaiian Islands are at the end of a chain of underwater volcanoes.

In both texts, underline the things we can expect to see on the ocean floor.

In one of the texts, highlight the sentence that shows how little we know about the ocean floor.

In both texts, circle the name of the highest mountain on Earth.

In both texts, color the height of the tallest mountain on Earth.

In one of the texts, highlight the name of underwater volcanoes.

The ocean floor is a mysterious world waiting to be explored. We know more about the surface of the moon and our closest planets! What we do know, however, is that the ocean floor has similar features to those found on land, such as mountains, volcanoes, and deep trenches.

The tallest mountain in the world actually starts on the ocean floor. It's Mount Kea in Hawaii, which is about 14,000 feet above sea level. But below sea level it measures almost 16,000 feet, making it slightly higher than Mount Everest.

1 What information do **both texts** give us about the features found on the ocean floor?

_____

_____

2 What information do **both texts** give us about the highest mountain in the world?

_____

_____

3 What extra information does **one of the texts** give us about the Hawaiian Islands?

_____

_____

RI.4.9 Integrate information from two texts on the same topic in order to write or speak about the subject knowledgeably.

Tricky words

Some words are trickier to spell than others. Sometimes we add letters that are not supposed to be there. Sometimes we leave out letters. Sometimes we write letters in the wrong order.

List

1 Write the word.

who _____

whose _____

across _____

busy _____

answer _____

once _____

usual _____

guilty _____

forty _____

writing _____

already _____

interest _____

therefore _____

question _____

doesn't _____

haven't _____

material _____

mention _____

breathe _____

position _____

2 Name.

a _____ b _____

3 Chunks. Rearrange the chunks to make a list word.

a read al y _____

b o se wh _____

c il ty gu _____

d st ion que _____

e ing wr it _____

f al mat i er _____

g n't do es _____

h i ion pos t _____

4 Complete each sentence with a list word.

a They wondered _____ had left the flowers.

b The bakery is _____ the street from the florist.

c I ask a _____ when I don't understand something.

d I couldn't finish sewing my pants because I ran out of _____.

e I ran downstairs to _____ the phone.

f I felt _____ for taking my sister's money.

g _____ upon a time there was a lonely frog.

h Humans cannot _____ underwater.

Tricky words

1 **Revise your spelling list from page 179.** Underline the mistakes.
Write the word correctly.

a It was raining; therefour we had to play inside. _____

b Wonce upon a time there lived a handsome prince. _____

c I havn't been to a circus before. _____

d We were so busie we forgot to eat lunch. _____

e I was so scared that I forgot to brethe. _____

f She had a lot of intrest in gardening. _____

g We had to swim akross the lake. _____

h I grew frustrated when he wouldn't anser me. _____

Challenge words

2 **Write the word.**

perhaps _____

possible _____

especially _____

favorite _____

suppose _____

neighbor _____

pollution _____

probably _____

address _____

purpose _____

3 **Word clues.** Which challenge word means?

a waste in the environment

_____

b where you live _____

c particularly _____

d maybe, possibly _____

e think, believe _____

f a reason or plan _____

g liked more than others

_____

h someone who lives nearby

_____

4 **Complete the sentence.**

a Spring is my _____ season.

b Solar powered cars could be a good way to cut down on _____.

c I gave her my _____ so she could come to the party.

d From the look of those dark clouds, it will _____ rain soon.

e Our _____ lets us pick lemons from his lemon tree.

Exclamation points for effect

Exclamation points (!) can be used

- at the end of a strong command or interjection; e.g., Be quiet! Ouch!
- to express excitement, surprise, admiration, or any other strong emotion; e.g., I was so upset! This cake is delicious!

WARNING! Exclamation points lose their effectiveness if you overuse them.

1 **In the following sentences, replace three of the periods with an exclamation point.**

a   A python is a type of reptile.

b   Get that snake out of my library immediately.

c   That is the most beautiful snake I've ever seen.

d   I found a book on snakes in the library.

e   Snakes alive. Are you trying to give me a heart attack?

2 **Circle three unnecessary exclamation points in the following passage.**

The sun was high in the sky, with not a cloud in sight! Trudging up the mountain path was becoming more and more difficult. Would they ever reach the legendary cave, and the treasure it supposedly contained?

Suddenly a large, black, winged creature landed on the path in front of them.

"Follow me!" it roared.

The men drew back in terror, but the creature had already started moving up the mountain and they felt compelled to follow it.

When the creature finally alighted, the men found themselves at the entrance to a large cave. The creature indicated with a nod of its head that they should go inside. Hesitantly, the men obeyed!

Slowly, their eyes became accustomed to the darkness and they were able to take stock of their surroundings!

"Look!" shouted one of the men. "Over there!"

3 **Change the following sentence so that it shows excitement. Use an exclamation point for effect.**

She is excited about going to the fair.

I can't wait _____

To the Limit

Read the passage.

In paragraph 1, underline a statement that we can prove is true.

In paragraph 2, highlight the words that express an opinion.

In paragraph 1, color a sentence that expresses an opinion.

In paragraph 3, underline two facts.

Some people think that plunging down the side of a mountain on a pair of skis is the most exciting feeling in the world. People who do this are called speed skiers. They can reach speeds of 150 miles an hour.

It takes cool nerves and top-notch protection to be a speed skier. Rocks, boulders, and trees can be deadly, so helmets are essential. Avalanches can also be a danger, so you need to carry a special light. Then you can be found and dug out of the snow if you are buried by an avalanche.

Brothers Simone and Ivan Origone of Italy are world champion speed skiers. In 2016, Ivan set off down Chabrieres piste in the French resort of Vars. By the time he reached the bottom, Ivan had set a new world record of 156.424 miles per hour.

1 Are the following statements **facts**, or **opinions**? Write **F** next to the facts and **O** next to the opinions.

a   Speed skiers reach speeds of 150 miles per hour. _____

b   It takes cool nerves and top-notch protection to be a speed skier. _____

c   Speed skiers carry a special light. _____

d   Speed skiers wear helmets. _____

e   Some people think that speed skiing is exciting. _____

f   Simone and Ivan Origone come from Italy. _____

g   In 2016, Ivan Origone set a new world record for speed skiing. _____

To the Limit

Read the passage.

Highlight the two sentences that express facts.

Color the things that can be seen in caves.

Underline the writer's opinion of how caving makes you feel.

Caving takes us deep within the earth. It involves a lot of crawling, squeezing, sliding, and stooping, often in mud and water. It is not for people who are claustrophobic or who want to keep their clothes clean.

But caving gives you the most amazing sights: gigantic chambers and deep black holes, underground lakes and rivers, and beautiful stalagmites and stalactites. Perhaps best of all, it makes you feel that you are in a place where no one else has been before.

(Circle) the word that expresses an opinion about the sights in caves.

Put a box around the word that expresses an opinion about stalagmites and stalactites.

1️⃣ In the passage, what **three facts** has the writer given us?

a _____

_____

b _____

_____

c _____

_____

2️⃣ In the passage, what **three opinions** has the writer expressed?

_____

_____

_____

_____

_____

Suffix: ly

Adding **ly** to an adjective turns it into an adverb; e.g., slow → slow**ly**.

If the adjective has *two or more syllables* and ends in **y**, change the **y** to **i** if there is a <u>consonant before it</u>; e.g., an/gr**y** → angr**ily**.

If the adjective ends in **le**, change **le** to **ly**; e.g., simp**le** → simp**ly**. If the adjective ends in **ic**, add **ally**; e.g., bas**ic** → bas**ically**.

List ① **Write the word.**

happily _____

gently _____

simply _____

easily _____

angrily _____

publicly _____

humbly _____

heavily _____

visibly _____

luckily _____

sensibly _____

possibly _____

basically _____

comfortably _____

nobly _____

steadily _____

wearily _____

historically _____

reasonably _____

remarkably _____

② **Word building.** Add the suffix *ly* to build these words.

heavy	heavily
simple	
gentle	
happy	
visible	
sensible	
possible	
noble	
lucky	
comfortable	
easy	

③ **Missing letters.** Fill in the missing letters.

a bas _ _ _ _ _ _

b rem _ _ _ _ _ _ _

c hu _ _ _ _

d luc _ _ _ _

e sen _ _ _ _ _

f hap _ _ _ _

g rea _ _ _ _ _ _ _

h ge _ _ _ _

④ **Complete each sentence with a list word.**

a Tamara _____ lifted the box as it wasn't heavy.

b My sister _____ slammed the door closed.

c Dad sat _____ in his armchair with his feet up.

d I sank _____ onto my bed after dance practice.

e This is _____ the best pasta I have ever eaten!

f The modest girl _____ accepted her award.

184

L.4.2.D Spell grade-appropriate words correctly.

Suffix: ly

1 **Revise your spelling list from page 184.** Underline the mistakes.
Write the word correctly.

a The girl smiled happely when she saw her new kitten. _____

b His answer is basecally correct. _____

c Remarkebly, I managed to get to football practice on time. _____

d I had worked on my model plane steedily for three months. _____

e The directors wanted the movie to be hestorically accurate. _____

f The nurse jently removed the bandage. _____

g Major Thompson publikely announced the new training routine. _____

Challenge words

2 **Write the word.**

specifically   _____

frantically   _____

responsibly   _____

automatically   _____

dramatically   _____

systematically   _____

enthusiastically _____

primarily   _____

necessarily   _____

ordinarily   _____

3 **Hidden words.** Find the challenge word.

a drautomaticallyl _____

b vonecessarilydja _____

c spfranticallysdjfi _____

d kdresponsiblynd _____

e opsspecificallys _____

f adramaticallysk _____

g asordinarilysfnli _____

h sdnprimarilyosfp _____

i senthusiasticallyt _____

4 **Complete each sentence.**

a I _____ asked for no sprinkles on my ice cream.

b I _____ took my shoes off after entering the house.

c I _____ organized my video game collection.

d She _____ agreed to help us decorate before the party.

e We began to clean _____ before all the guests arrived.

Compound and complex sentences

A **compound** sentence has **two or more main clauses**; e.g., The clouds **are gathering** and thunder **is rumbling** in the distance. Compound sentences are formed using the **conjunctions and, but, or**, and **so**.

A complex sentence has a **main clause** and a subordinate clause; e.g., The clouds, which are gathering in the distance, are dark and menacing. The subordinate clause depends on the main clause for its meaning.

Complex sentences are formed using:

- the **relative pronouns** who, whose, whom, which, and that.
- **conjunctions** like **after, although, because, before, if, unless, until, when**, and **while**.

1 **Complete each of the following sentences with a word from the box.**

| who | but | after | because | which | if | while | unless |

a   You will get a better time _____ you work harder.

b   I like to brush my teeth _____ I have eaten breakfast.

c   He won't give you a new pen _____ you ask for one.

d   I asked my friend, _____ is very artistic, to paint my portrait.

e   She sat in the waiting room _____ I talked to the doctor.

f   The ship, _____ is enormous, can carry thousands of passengers.

g   Nina likes adventures stories, _____ Max prefers science fiction.

h   I couldn't buy the computer game _____ I didn't have enough money.

2 **Join each of the following sentences with the conjunction in parentheses.**

a   I've had lunch. I'm still hungry. (but) _____

_____

b   I will visit them. They are at home. (if) _____

_____

c   I made an appointment. I went to see him. (before) _____

_____

d   I will feed the dog. You unpack the dishwasher. (while) _____

_____

L.4.2 Demonstrate command of the conventions of standard English punctuation when writing.

Technological Wonders

Compare and contrast

Compare and contrast information by looking for the similarities and differences between details in the text.

Read the passage.

Underline what type of waste fossil-fuel power stations produce.

Highlight what coal and oil are used to produce.

Color the word that tells what type of fuel coal and oil are.

Put a box around the metal from which nuclear energy is produced.

Circle what nuclear energy is used to produce.

Circle the type of waste nuclear power stations produce.

Nuclear energy is released from the nucleus of a uranium atom, a very dense metal found in the ground. Nuclear energy produces more than 11% of the world's electricity.

Supporters of nuclear energy argue that nuclear power stations are safe and much cleaner than fossil fuel power stations. However many countries are starting to rethink their nuclear energy programs due to disasters like Fukushima in 2011.

More than one-third of human-made greenhouse gases come from fossil-fuel power stations. As people continue to use coal and oil to produce electricity and fuel for transport, the amount of greenhouse gas emissions will increase. Nuclear power stations do not emit these gases, although they do produce radioactive waste.

Circle the correct answer/s for each question.

1 In what way are nuclear power stations and fossil-fuel power stations **similar**?

a Both produce greenhouse gases.   b Both produce electricity.

c Both use coal and oil.   d Both help to clean the air.

2 In what two ways are nuclear power stations and fossil-fuel power stations **different**?

a They use different methods to produce electricity.

b They use different types of fossil-fuels.

c They affect the environment differently.

d They produce different types of energy.

Technological Wonders

Read the passage.

Read the full text

Technological Wonders

<u>Underline</u> how Charles Lindbergh's flight was different from John Alcock's and Arthur Brown's.

Put a box around the name of the first woman to fly across the Atlantic.

Important Dates in the History of Flight

1903: Orville and Wilbur Wright completed the first flight in an aircraft.

1919: John Alcock and Arthur Brown completed the first nonstop flight across the Atlantic Ocean.

1927: Charles Lindbergh completed the first solo, nonstop flight across the Atlantic Ocean.

1928: Amelia Earhart became the first woman to fly across the Atlantic Ocean.

1961: Yuri Gagarin became the first person to travel in space.

1969: Neil Armstrong and Buzz Aldrin became the first people to walk on the moon.

Color the name of the ocean Alcock, Brown, Lindbergh, and Earhart flew across.

Highlight how Neil Armstrong and Buzz Aldrin's experience in space was different from Yuri Gagarin's.

1 How was the Wright brothers' and Alcock and Brown's experience with flight **similar**?

_____

_____

2 What was **similar** about the flights of Lindbergh and Earhart?

_____

_____

3 What was the main **difference** between the flights of Yuri Gagarin, and Neil Armstrong and Buzz Aldrin?

_____

_____

RI.4.1 Refer to details and examples in a text when explaining what the text says explicitly and when drawing inferences from the text.

Letter patterns: cc, xc

When the letters **cc** come after a vowel, and <u>before e or i</u>, the second **c** has a soft sound; e.g., a**cc**ept, a**cc**ident. It has a hard sound when it comes <u>before consonants and other vowels</u>; e.g., a**cc**laim, a**cc**ount.

When the letters **xc** come after a vowel, and <u>before e or i</u>, **c** has a soft sound; e.g., e**xc**ess, e**xc**ite. It has a hard sound when it comes <u>before consonants and other vowels</u>; e.g., e**xc**laim, e**xc**use.

List   ① Write the word.

accent _____

accept _____

excellent _____

excel _____

excite _____

accuse _____

exclaim _____

accident _____

success _____

excuse _____

exceed _____

accustom _____

acclaim _____

account _____

accost _____

excess _____

accelerate _____

exclude _____

excavate _____

excursion _____

② Sort the words.

CC	XC

③ Chunks. Rearrange the chunks to make a list word.

a   la im cc a   _____

b   ost a cc   _____

c   cc us tom a   _____

d   cc ess su   _____

e   cell ex ent   _____

④ Meaning. Which list word means?

a   To blame someone for a crime or an offense   _____

b   To hollow out or make a hole by digging   _____

c   An unintentional or unexpected event   _____

d   To increase speed   _____

e   A short trip   _____

f   To leave out   _____

Letter patterns: cc, xc

1 **Revise your spelling list from page 189.** Find the opposite.

a failure _____

b refuse _____

c slow down _____

d include _____

2 **Missing letters.** Write the missing letters.

a _____lent   b _____sion

c _____ount   d _____rate

e _____ost   f _____tom

g _____ude   h _____cept

i _____cent   j _____cel

Challenge words

3 **Write the word.**

eccentric _____

accessory _____

accumulate _____

excavation _____

exceptional _____

accidentally _____

excerpt _____

accompany _____

accomplish _____

excruciating _____

4 **Word clues.** Which challenge word means?

a to go with someone _____

b to collect or gather _____

c odd or peculiar _____

d extremely painful _____

e complete successfully

_____

f hat, bag, scarf _____

g by mistake _____

h short section taken from a book or film

_____

5 **Complete each sentence.**

a When I broke my arm I was in _____ pain for weeks.

b I _____ tripped and spilled my drink all over the floor.

c A purple necklace is her favorite _____.

d Before bed I read an _____ from my favorite book.

e My mom will _____ me to the doctor.

f I felt confident I would _____ all my tasks.

g I was hoping to _____ a large collection of shoes.

h There are three archaeologists overseeing the _____.

Spoken and written English

Spoken English is usually more informal than written English. However, we often use formal language when we speak to people in authority or those we don't know very well, and we use informal language when we write emails or text messages to friends.

1 **Color the more formal expression in the following pairs.**

- **a** movie   film
- **b** child   kid
- **c** will not   won't
- **d** yeah   yes
- **e** goodbye   see ya
- **f** hey   good morning

2 **Replace each underlined word with a more formal expression from the box.**

- **a** Sorry, I <u>gotta</u> go now. _____
- **b** This food is really <u>yummy</u>! _____
- **c** She told us not to be <u>cheeky</u>. _____
- **d** The exhibition was <u>awesome</u>! _____
- **e** I will <u>get in touch with</u> him tomorrow. _____

contact
tasty
impolite
wonderful
have to

3 **Circle the correct expression in parentheses to complete this formal letter of apology.**

Dear Mr. Cooper

(I'd/I would) like to (apologize/say sorry) to you for (allowing my dog to/ letting my dog) go into your garden and (destroy/smash down) your plants. I know it took (ages/a long time) for those plants to grow and that you were (very proud of/crazy about) them. You must have been (real mad/very angry) when you saw what Spotty had done.

I hope you will forgive (me and Spotty/Spotty and me). If there is anything I can do to (make it up to/repay) you, (please/just) let me know.

(Cheers/Yours sincerely)
Jordan Redman

L.4.3.C Differentiate between contexts that call for formal English and situations where informal discourse is appropriate.

191

Biggest, Highest, Fastest

Read the passage.

Circle how many insects there are for each human.

Highlight the number of new species of insect that are discovered each year.

Put a box around how many locusts there are in a swarm.

Underline how much a locust eats in a day.

Color the damage locusts can cause.

What makes a small bug big? It's all to do with some very big numbers. Scientists have worked out that there could be 10 quintillion insects alive at any one time. That's 10,000,000,000,000,000,000 bugs or 1.6 billion of them for every one of us. And about 8,000 new kinds are discovered each year.

Some insects, such as locusts, move in huge hungry groups called swarms. Swarms can contain thousands of millions of locusts. To stay alive, every locust needs to eat its own body weight in food each day. A swarm of locusts strips trees bare and gobbles up crops. There is nothing left after a locust swarm has passed.

Circle the correct answer for each question.

1 Which is the best **conclusion?**

  a Humans outnumber insects.
  b Insects are big bugs.
  c Insects outnumber humans.
  d Insects have long life spans.

2 Which sentence is the best **clue** to question 1's answer?

  a There are 1.6 billion of them for every one of us.
  b About 8,000 new kinds are discovered each year.
  c It's all to do with some very big numbers.
  d What makes a small bug big?

3 Which is the best **conclusion**? Locusts ...

  a help the environment.
  b kill insect pests.
  c weigh a lot.
  d destroy crops and trees.

4 Which group of words is the best **clue** to question 3's answer?

  a body weight   b hungry groups   c nothing left d thousands of millions

  RI.4.1 Refer to details and examples in a text when explaining what the text says explicitly and when drawing inferences from the text.

Biggest, Highest, Fastest

Read the
full text

*Biggest,
Highest,
Fastest*

Read the passage.

Underline three
ways that animals
catch their prey.

Highlight the
sentence that best
sums up the way
animals depend
on each other
for survival.

The slash of a claw, the flick of a
tongue, or a strike from out of nowhere
can mean life or sudden death.

There's a need for speed in the animal
world. All creatures are part of a food
chain. The trick here is catching what
you like to eat but not getting caught
by what likes to eat you.

But fast isn't always about making a
quick getaway. To get its food, the
hummingbird flaps very fast to stay still!

Put a box
around two words
that are opposite in
meaning.

Circle how a
hummingbird uses
speed to get its food.

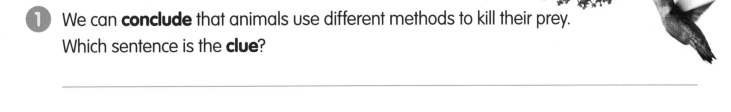

1 We can **conclude** that animals use different methods to kill their prey.
Which sentence is the **clue**?

_____

_____

_____

2 Which sentence **suggests** that most animals are both predators and prey?

_____

_____

_____

3 What overall **conclusion** can we draw about survival in the animal kingdom?

_____

_____

_____

_____

Greek origins

Many English words come from Greek words; e.g., **micro** means *small* in Greek and from micro we get **micro**scope, **micro**chip, and **micro**phone.

List

zoo

logo

octopus

microscope

microphone

telephone

microchip

telescope

octave

October

geology

octagon

catalog

periscope

television

dialogue

phonetic

epilogue

homophone

monologue

1 Write the word.

_____

_____

_____

_____

_____

_____

_____

_____

_____

_____

_____

_____

_____

_____

_____

_____

_____

_____

_____

_____

2 Name.

a _____ b _____

c _____ d _____

3 Missing letters. Fill in the missing letters.

a homo _____   b geo _____

c m_____scope   d mono_____

e t_____scope   f _____pus

g phon_____   h _____chip

4 Word clues. Which list word means?

a a device to make sound louder _____

b a musical term; eight notes apart _____

c used on a submarine _____

d a conversation between two people _____

e the section at the end of a book _____

f a symbol to identify a brand or company _____

g used to see planets _____

h small electronic device programmed with circuits _____

L.4.2.D Spell grade-appropriate words correctly.

Greek origins

1 **Revise your spelling list from page 194.** Underline the mistake. Write the word correctly.

a The astronomer gazed through her tellescope. _____

b The oktopus swam quickly into a small cave. _____

c Dad told us to switch off the tellevision. _____

d I recited a whole monologe without forgetting any words. _____

e Her voice went up an octaive when she discovered the mess. _____

f We put a mikrochip in our new puppy. _____

g I flipped through the cataloge to find the best deals on laptops. _____

h The captain looked through the periskope. _____

Challenge words

2 **Write the word.**

democrat _____

geographic _____

democracy _____

octahedron _____

zoologist _____

symphony _____

xylophone _____

saxophone _____

epidemic _____

chronological _____

3 **Word clues.** Which challenge word means?

a a supporter of democracy

_____

b consecutive order _____

c a form of government _____

d outbreak of a disease _____

e played by an orchestra _____

f eight-sided 3D object _____

g an instrument with wooden bars played with small hammers

_____

4 **Complete the sentence.**

a An _____ is a three-dimensional shape with eight flat surfaces.

b I blew into the _____ but no noise came out.

c I used wooden mallets to play the _____.

d The _____ was checking up on all the sick animals.

e I placed my photos in _____ order.

Punctuate a variety of sentences

> Punctuation helps readers understand writing.
> - Periods (.), question marks (?), and exclamation points (!) end sentences; e.g., My name is Kim. What is your name? What a great name that is!
> - Commas (,) separate parts of a sentence and items in a list; e.g., Although he's a small boy, he is very strong. Today I traveled on a bus, a train, and a ferry.
> - Apostrophes (') show ownership and where letters have been left out of words; e.g., That is the boy's vest. I should've known he'd bring his little brother with him.

1 **Fill in a period, question mark, or exclamation point at the end of each sentence.**

a   When are you going to finish your project

b   What an adventure that was

c   The last time I went on a boat, I was seasick

d   When I'm overseas, I'll email you every day

e   What is the matter with your cat

f   How amazing was that ride

2 **Use a red pen to correct the punctuation in the following sentences.**

a   The knifes handle is solid gold.

b   They shoul'dve finished their work by now.

c   I like the red dress with the white spots the best?

d   I left my dogs collar at my friend's house.

e   While I was at my tennis lesson. my little brother played with my toys.

3 **Fill in the punctuation marks in the following sentences.**

Have you seen Marks new puppy Its so cute. Im going to ask my parents if I can have one too

L.4.2 Demonstrate command of the conventions of standard English punctuation when writing.

Spelling

You have learned about:

- prefixes: re, de, pre
- suffixes: able, ible
- suffix: ly
- suffixes: ment, ship, hood, dom
- Latin origins
- letter patterns: cc, xc
- endings: ery, ary, ory
- tricky words
- Greek origins

....

1 **In each sentence, the spelling error has been <u>underlined</u>. Write the correct spelling.** 2 marks

a Scuba divers use a special tank so they can <u>brethe</u> underwater. _____

b My dad is going to turn <u>fourty</u> next month. _____

c We chopped onions, <u>celary</u>, and carrot for the soup. _____

d We can learn a lot from reading books about our <u>histery</u>. _____

2 **Which word correctly completes this sentence?** 1 mark

Alex used the _____ to measure two cups of flour for his cake.

a scalle   b scaling   c scaled   d scale

3 **This sentence has one word that is incorrect. Write the correct spelling.** 1 mark

If you answer this qustion correctly, you'll take home the grand prize. _____

4 **Complete the words with ment, ship, or hood.** 1 mark

a enjoy _ _ _ _   b adult _ _ _ _   c excite _ _ _ _   d leader _ _ _ _

5 **Circle the correct verb to complete each sentence.** 2 marks

a We skipped (happy, happily, happiness) to meet Grandpa at the station.

b It's (sensible, sensibly, sense) to cross the road at the traffic lights.

c "But it's time for lunch!" shouted the chef (angry, angrily, angriness).

d Before the long flight, we made ourselves (comfortable, comfortably, comfort).

6 **The words octagon, octave, and octopus are all words with Greek origins. In Greek, what does octo- mean?** 1 mark

a eight   b music   c shape   d animal

7 **Correctly complete each word with either _cc_ or _xc_.** 2 marks

a e _ _ ellent   b su _ _ ess   c e _ _ ess   d a _ _ use

Your score

10

Grammar

You have learned about:

- subordinate clauses
- relative clauses
- using punctuation for effect
- relative pronouns
- compound and complex sentences
- spoken and written English
- relative adverbs
- questions and exclamations
- punctuating sentences

1 **Draw lines to match the main and subordinate clauses.** 2 marks

Main clause	Subordinate clause
a You can go to the concert	unless someone helps me.
b She was shivering	until someone wins.
c We will keep on playing	because she was cold.
d I won't be able to lift the box	if you buy a ticket.

2 **In the following sentences, underline the relative pronouns.** 2 marks

a The tree, which is at the bottom of the garden, sheds lots of leaves.

b The lady who knocked on our door was looking for her cat.

c The dog that ate the sausages is in the garden.

d I pointed to the man whose jacket it was.

3 **In each sentence, color the relative adverb and underline the noun it refers to.** 2 marks

a I went back to the building where I'd last seen them.

b My grandparents lived in a time when there were no cell phones.

4 **In each sentence, highlight the main clause and underline the relative clause.** 2 marks

a I called out to the girl who had dropped her book.

b Watch out for frogs that have brightly colored skins.

c She'll be able to tell me whose watch this is.

d We picked up the eggs which had fallen from the nest.

5 **Write whether the following are compound or complex sentences.** 2 marks

a I've finished my lunch, but I'm still hungry. _____

b I'll help you when I've finished my chores. _____

c I dropped the plate because it was hot. _____

d He washed the shirt and he ironed it. _____

Grammar

6 Complete each sentence with an exclamation point or question mark. 2 marks

   a What brilliant colors she has used

   b What colors will she use in that painting

   c How many colors does she need

   d How amazing is that painting

7 Make the following passage more interesting by changing two periods to exclamation points. 2 marks

> Tess held out her arm and Ari slipped on the wristband.
>
> "Trust me, Tess," he said, "you're going to love New York." He grabbed her hand and yelled, "Three ... two ... one ... here we go."
>
> They skated up and off the ramp. They landed skating down a very different ramp. They were on the rooftop of a tall building in a sea of tall buildings.
>
> Tess spun around, staring at the skyline. "This place is MONSTROUS."

8 Circle the informal expression in each sentence. Replace it with a more formal expression. 2 marks

   a Two cops knocked on our door. _____

   b There are ten kids in my dance class. _____

   c My friend is real smart. _____

   d Me and Mark are going to the park. _____

9 Write each sentence with the correct punctuation. 4 marks

   a she picked up the childs toy _____

     _____

   b how did you get here asked the man _____

     _____

Your score

☐

20

What is Pollution?

Read the passage and then use the comprehension skills you have learned to answer the questions.

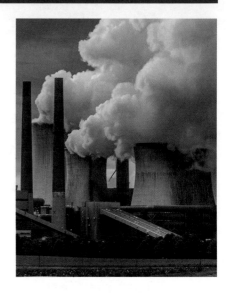

Pollution occurs when rubbish and poisons contaminate the air, water, or soil. Pollution is harmful to people, animals, and plants. It can cause disease or death.

The air becomes polluted when poisonous gases, dust, chemical fumes, and smoke are released into the atmosphere. Burning fossil fuels like coal and oil is a major cause of air pollution. Power stations produce electricity by burning coal. Cars, trucks, and buses use fuels that come from oil.

Water becomes polluted when poisons enter our rivers and oceans. These pollutants kill the plants and animals that live in the water. Sometimes the oil from ships and underwater oil wells spills into the sea. The oil floating on top of the water sticks to the feathers of birds and they cannot fly. Fish are unable to breathe beneath the oil-covered water.

Careless dumping of rubbish is pollution. Flies breeding in rotting rubbish can spread disease. Animals may become sick from eating the rubbish. They can hurt themselves on sharp objects, wire, and broken glass.

The soil can become polluted when farmers use chemicals like pesticides, weed killers, and fertilizers on their crops. Animals eating grass grown on polluted land can become sick. Poisons that pass through the food chain can affect people's health.

Noise is another form of pollution. Constant noise is tiring and stressful. Loud, harsh noises can permanently damage hearing.

Many countries have laws to stop or cut down on pollution. However, we are all responsible for keeping our environment free of pollution.

1 Which of the following can cause air pollution? 1 mark   LITERAL

    a spilled oil   **b** broken glass

    c loud noises   **d** chemical fumes

2 What effect does air pollution have on humans? Air pollution can make humans ... 1 mark   INFERENTIAL

   a restless.   b sick.

   c anxious.   d confused.

3 Give a text clue to support your answer to question 2. 2 marks   CRITICAL

_____

_____

4 How do cars, trucks, and buses contribute to air pollution? Cars, trucks, and buses ... 1 mark   INFERENTIAL

   a release fumes into the atmosphere.   b churn up lots of dust.

   c spill oil on the roads.   d make a lot of noise.

5 Where will pollution from cars be worst? 1 mark   CRITICAL

   a in a large city   b in a country town

   c on a farm   d on a small island

6 Why are fish unable to breathe if the water is covered in oil? The oil ... 1 mark   CRITICAL

   a sucks the oxygen out of the water.   b creates too much oxygen in the water.

   c prevents oxygen from entering the water.   d causes the water to evaporate.

7 Why do farmers use fertilizers on their crops? 1 mark   CRITICAL

   a to destroy weeds   b to remove nutrients from the soil

   c to boost plant growth   d to destroy pests

8 How can people who work in noisy places protect their hearing? 2 marks   CRITICAL

_____

_____

Your score

☐

10

Your Review 4 Scores

Spelling		Grammar	Comprehension		Total
☐	+	☐	+ ☐	=	☐
10		**20**	**10**		**40**

Week 1, Day 1
Pg 2

> Lots of children heard about the goats and came to visit. Morecambe and Wise put their heads down and (butted them in all directions)
>
> The children thought it was great fun—that is, the ones that got away did. The children who didn't escape went home crying and told their mothers.
>
> Mr. Kent smiled when he saw what was happening. "These goats are as good as a watchdog," he said. "This'll put a stop to whoever is stealing our strawberries."
>
> Mr. Kent wasn't so happy the next day. He was at the dam. He leaned forward, then called excitedly to Mrs. Kent. "We've got some baby crabs! Hurray!"

1 *Answers will vary. Ask children to talk through responses.*

2 *Answers will vary. Ask children to talk through responses.*

Week 1, Day 2
Pg 3

> When Mrs. Kent went in to wake the children, she was terribly (shocked.)
>
> "The children aren't here!" she cried to Mr. Kent. "Where could they be?"
>
> Mr. and Mrs. Kent looked everywhere. They looked inside the house and outside the house.
>
> Morecambe starting butting his head against Mr. Kent as he searched near the shed.
>
> Wise started pushing against Mrs. Kent while she peered under the car.
>
> "The goats are trying to tell us something," said Mr. Kent.
>
> "Let's untie them and see what they do," replied Mrs. Kent.

1 *Answers will vary. Suggested answer:*
I think the goats are going to help Mr. and Mrs. Kent find the missing children.

2 *Answers will vary. Suggested answer:*
I made this prediction based on the dialogue between Mr. and Mrs. Kent. Mr. Kent says, "The goats are trying to tell us something." I connected this dialogue to other books I have read. The author often leaves clues for the reader and Mr. Kent's suggestion made me think maybe the animals had seen which way the missing children went and would be able to lead Mr. and Mrs. Kent.

Week 1, Day 3
Pg 4

1 Check for correct spelling of each word.

2 a radio **b** throne **c** spade **d** spine

3 Missing letters are <u>underlined</u>
   a b<u>o</u>ld **b** <u>a</u>while **c** <u>o</u>nly **d** br<u>o</u>ken
   e str<u>i</u>ke **f** r<u>a</u>dio **g** <u>e</u>state **h** al<u>o</u>ne
   i expl<u>o</u>de **j** <u>s</u>urprise

4 a radio **b** ninth **c** wild **d** spade
   e alone **f** surprise

Week 1, Day 4
Pg 5

1 a <u>spayd</u> spade **b** <u>moste</u> most
   c <u>suprise</u> surprise **d** tayst taste
   e <u>nineth</u> ninth **f** <u>floot</u> flute
   g <u>devide</u> divide **h** <u>wyld</u> wild

2 Check for correct spelling of each word.

3 a devoted **b** imitate **c** satellite
   d barricade **e** ozone **f** unite
   g idle **h** phrase **i** produce
   j suppose

4 a produce **b** phrase **c** satellite
   d suppose **e** ozone

Week 1, Day 5
Pg 6

1 a knife **b** cheese **c** Grand Canyon
   d mountain/Mount Everest

2 a The White House **b** zebra
   c Golden Gate Bridge

3 a Common nouns: elephant, pelican, computer, table, branch
   b Proper nouns: Saturday, Joseph, April, Brazil, Charlie

Week 2, Day 1
Pg 7

> Tessa's Great Grandma Em had a face like a sheet of scrunched up newspaper. Great Grandpop Alfred teased her lots.
>
> "You look like a (hippopotamus) that has been bathing in the river too long," he said at breakfast.
>
> "The bags under your eyes could carry the treasure from a sunken pirate ship," he said at lunch.

1 d **2** b **3** c **4** a **5** c

Week 2, Day 2
Pg 8

> By the time the big day arrived, Great Gran's skin was as smooth as whipped cream, her cheeks were as rosy as ripe strawberries, and her eyes were like rich dark chocolate drops.
>
> "You're as lovely as the day I first saw you running across the field from the Maloney's prize bull," said Great Grandpop as he waltzed her around the living room.

1 *Answers will vary. Suggested answer:*
that her skin is pale, soft, and creamy

2 *Answers will vary. Ask children to talk through responses.*

3 *Answers will vary. Suggested answer:*
her eyes are beautiful and dark

4 *Answers will vary. Suggested answer:*
Great Gran's skin is whipped cream

Week 2, Day 3
Pg 9

1 Check for correct spelling of each word.

2 a jewel **b** fruit **c** cashews **d** suit

3 a cashew **b** juice **c** continue
   d avenue **e** nephew

4 a nephew **b** chew **c** cashew **d** value
   e avenue **f** jewel **g** rescue **h** clue
   i fruit **j** threw **k** argue **l** stew

Week 2, Day 4
Pg 10

1

ew	ue	ui
dew	true	suit
blew	clue	fruit
skew	rescue	juice
stew	venue	
chew	argue	
threw	continue	
jewel	value	
nephew	avenue	
cashew		

2 Check for correct spelling of each word.

3 a sluice **b** pewter **c** mildew **d** residue
   e sinew **f** askew **g** jewelry **h** pursue

4 a jewelry **b** askew **c** residue

Week 2, Day 5
Pg 11

1 a <u>we</u> oliver **b** <u>myra</u> i **c** <u>we</u> beaufort
   d <u>he</u> wednesday **e** <u>the</u> mississippi jackson
   f <u>our</u> bailey **g** <u>my</u> october

2 Yesterday I went to the zoo with my friends, Simon and Lauren. We had a great time looking at all the animals. Our favorites were the chimpanzees and gorillas. We also liked the bird show.

3 a *Answers will vary. Suggested answer:*
   the Natural History Museum when I am in New York.
   b *Answers will vary. Suggested answer:*
   Toby that likes to dig holes in the garden.

Week 3, Day 1
Pg 12

> Anita unfolded a map of Japan.
>
> "It says the capital of Japan is (Tokyo) That's where we're going." She read on, "Japan is made up of four main islands and over 3,000 little ones." Anita marked Tokyo, on the island of Honshu, with a red spot.
>
> In the corner of the map Jason pointed to a white flag with a red circle in the middle. "That's the Japanese flag," he said. "The word Japan actually means source of the sun."

> Japan is a country in the Pacific Ocean. It consists of four main islands and thousands of smaller ones. The capital city, (Tokyo) is on the island of Honshu.
>
> Japan is known as the *Land of the Rising Sun.* This is because its name means sun origin.
>
> Japan is on the Pacific Ring of Fire. It experiences over 1,500 earthquakes every year. In 2011, a huge earthquake and tsunami caused a lot of damage.

1 a, b, d, f, h

Week 3, Day 2
Pg 13

> Jason looked out the train window. Beyond the rice fields he could see a huge snow-capped mountain.
>
> "That mountain looks like an old volcano."
>
> "It is. Japan is full of volcanoes," said Toshi. "That's Mt. Fuji, Japan's most famous mountain."
>
> Jason pulled an instant camera out of his bag and took a photo. On the bottom he wrote 'Mount Fuji, JAPAN—famous old volcano.'

> Mount Fuji is Japan's highest and most famous mountain. It has been worshipped as a sacred mountain for centuries.
>
> Mount Fuji is an active volcano. It last erupted in 1708.
>
> A good way to view Mount Fuji is from the train on the trip between Tokyo and Osaka. Tourists can often be seen taking photographs of Mount Fuji from the train windows.

1 Mount Fuji is Japan's most famous mountain. It is an old volcano.

2 It is a snow capped mountain and it is the highest in Japan. Mount Fuji has been worshipped as a sacred mountain for centuries. It is still an active volcano and it last erupted in 1708.
3 *Answers will vary. Ask children to talk through responses.*

Week 3, Day 3
Pg 14
1 Check for correct spelling of each word.
2 a Earth **b** beard
3 a yearn **b** lair **c** beard **d** pearl
 e pioneer **f** Earth **g** weary **h** dreary
 i prairie **j** eerie
4 a search **b** earnings **c** research
 d Earth **e** prairie **f** eerie

Week 3, Day 4
Pg 15
1

air	eer		ear
lair	steer	hear	clear
fairly	eerie	smear	weary
despair	pioneer	early	yearn
prairie		beard	earnings
		Earth	research
		pearl	dreary
		search	

2 Check for correct spelling of each word.
3 a millionaire **b** buccaneer **c** questionnaire
 d rehearse **e** earnest **f** puppeteer
 g engineer **h** veneer **i** auctioneer
 j volunteer
4 a puppeteer **b** rehearse **c** engineer
 d volunteer **e** auctioneer

Week 3, Day 5
Pg 16
1 a laughter **b** memory **c** luck
 d comfort **e** fascination **f** curiosity
2 a common **b** abstract **c** common
 d proper **e** abstract **f** proper
3 a *Answers will vary. Suggested answer:* Watching a beautiful sunset over a beach gives me great joy.
 b *Answers will vary. Suggested answer:* The children had the freedom to choose which movie they watched on Saturday night.
 c *Answers will vary. Suggested answer:* Our new neighbors thanked us for our kindness.

Week 4, Day 1
Pg 17

Narrator: Long ago in the Dreaming, when the world was formed Tiddalik, the frog woke very (thirsty) one morning.
Tiddalik: I need water, I need water, I need water …
Narrator: So Tiddalik drank all the water he could find.
Tiddalik: [gulp] [gulp] [gulp] [gulp]
Narrator: He drank so much that every billabong and creek and every river and stream was emptied.

1 d   **2** b   **3** a

Week 4, Day 2
Pg 18

Narrator: Suddenly, Nabunum the eel, whose home had dried out because the water had gone, slithered up to Tiddalik.
Nabunum: Time for you to laugh, froggy.
Narrator: Nabunum began to dance, slowly at first, then faster and faster, wriggling into all sorts of shapes, knots and twists. It worked! Tiddalik started giggling.
Kookaburra: I think he's going to burst.
Wombat: Stand back, here comes the water!

1 Nabunum danced to make Tiddalik laugh.
2 a Nabunum says, "time for you to laugh, froggy."
 b the Narrator explains how Nabunum dances slowly, then faster and faster, whilst wriggling into all sorts of shapes, knots, and twists
 c when the Narrator says, "It worked! Tiddalik started giggling.", the reader knows that was Nabunum's intention all along, to make himself seem foolish so Tiddalik would laugh

Week 4, Day 3
Pg 19
1 Check for correct spelling of each word.
2 a shrugging **b** throbbing **c** whizzing
 d humming **e** thudding **f** propping
 g stunning **h** chatting
3 Missing vowels are underlined
 a planning **b** scrubbing **c** trapping
 d digging **e** hopping **f** shrugging
 g whipping **h** humming **i** grinning
 j chopping **k** swimming **l** whizzing
 m wrapping **n** stunning **o** thudding
 p running
4 a swimming **b** grinning **c** running
 d digging

Week 4, Day 4
Pg 20
1 a chopping **b** dripping **c** chatting
 d digging **e** swimming **f** running
 g planning
2 Check for correct spelling of each word.
3 a forbidding **b** committing **c** permitting
 d transmitting **e** worshipping **f** submitting
 g equipping **h** formatting **i** regretting
4 a forgetting **b** regretting **c** formatting
 d submitting **e** worshipping **f** equipping

Week 4, Day 5
Pg 21
1 ✓ a, d, e, f, g, j
2 a Alice's adventures in wonderland
 b the black stallion **c** zlateh the goat
 d dust of snow
 e where the mountain meets the moon
 f the making of a hurricane
 g seeing eye to eye
 h underground railroad
3 a women Women **b** recipes Recipes
 c A a **d** Of of
 e geographic Geographic

Week 5, Day 1
Pg 22

Long ago, (a turtle) lived in a pond with (two swans.) The turtle loved to talk. After a long drought, the pond dried up. The two swans realized they would have to find another pond.
"Don't leave me!" begged the turtle.
"But you can't fly," said the swans. "How can you come with us?" The turtle pleaded and pleaded. The swans at last came up with an idea.

1 b   **2** c   **3** d   **4** c   **5** b

Week 5, Day 2
Pg 23

When they flew high, the turtle wanted to say "Look at the beautiful view!" but he remembered the swans' warning. They passed over a small town. People looked up and shouted, "Look at that silly turtle!" The turtle wanted to cry out, "Mind your own business," but he again remembered the warning. As they flew on, more villagers spotted them. People began pointing and crying out, "Crazy swans! Crazy turtle!" The turtle couldn't stand it any longer. He yelled out, "Go away foolish people!" But he let go of the stick and fell to the ground, landing on his back and cracking his shell into a thousand pieces.

1 "Look at the beautiful view!"
2 over a small town
3 when the people began pointing and crying out
4 he fell to the ground, landing on his back and cracking his shell into a thousand pieces

Week 5, Day 3
Pg 24
1 Check for correct spelling of each word.
2 a answers **b** radishes **c** losses
 d ladders **e** kangaroos **f** leashes
 g speeches **h** balloons
3 a visitors **b** kangaroos **c** speeches
 d minutes **e** authors **f** trumpets
4 a nurses **b** ladders **c** trumpets
 d leashes **e** kangaroos **f** winners

Week 5, Day 4
Pg 25
1 a balloons **b** radios **c** ladders
 d glasses
2 Check for correct spelling of each word.
3 a volcanoes **b** sandwiches **c** sombreros
 d topazes **e** gelatos **f** passengers
 g blemishes **h** referees **i** spectators
 j witnesses
4 a gelatos **b** passengers **c** blemishes
 d referees **e** spectators **f** witnesses

Week 5, Day 5
Pg 26
1 Color: him, she, itself, you, himself, them
2 a himself **b** I **c** themselves
 d ourselves **e** I **f** she **g** He
3 a itself **b** her/him **c** me **d** them **e** he

ANSWERS • Weeks 6–8

Week 6, Day 1
Pg 27

> Most homes received electricity during the ⟨early 1900's⟩. Rural homes had to wait longer. Many homes in developing countries still do not have electricity.
>
> Electricity changed the way homes worked. Electric ovens and heaters replaced gas and wood-burning stoves. Electric light bulbs replaced kerosene lamps and gas lights. Electric refrigerators replaced iceboxes. Electricity also led to the invention of the ⟨telephone⟩.

1 d   **2** a, d, f

Week 6, Day 2
Pg 28

> The layout of rooms in a home has changed as society has changed.
>
> As plumbing improved, bathrooms became rooms inside the home, rather than outside.
>
> Kitchens only became the centre of homes in the last 60 years. Filled with new appliances, they are no longer hidden rooms used for hard, dirty work. They are linked to open-plan living and dining areas.
>
> Informal living areas at the rear of homes replaced formal living rooms at the front. Living areas were linked to terraces and gardens to create outdoor rooms.

1 The layout of rooms in a home has changed as society has changed.
2 a bathrooms became rooms inside the home
 b kitchens moved to the centre and had new appliances
 c living areas moved to the back of homes where they could become linked to terraces and gardens to create outdoor rooms

Week 6, Day 3
Pg 29

1 Check for correct spelling of each word.
2 a price, dance, parcel, decide, except, cyclone, accept, success, prince, choice, princess, saucer, century
 b germ, digit, agent, large, legend, danger, energy
3 a success **b** danger **c** accept
4 a parcel **b** cyclone **c** saucer **d** price

Week 6, Day 4
Pg 30

1 a germ **b** prince **c** century
 d dance **e** price **f** digit
2 Check for correct spelling of each word.
3 a genius **b** surgery **c** allergic
 d message **e** emergency **f** rejoice
 g gigantic **h** accident **i** announce
4 a accident **b** celebrate **c** surgery
 d gigantic **e** announce **f** message

Week 6, Day 5
Pg 31

1 a has **b** wears **c** sit **d** are
 e drives **f** hammers **g** screams
2 a ⟨helps⟩ **b** ⟨jumps⟩ **c** ⟨fixes⟩ **d** ⟨washes⟩
 e ⟨arranges⟩ **f** ⟨walks⟩ **g** ⟨sings⟩ **h** ⟨claps⟩
 i ⟨flies⟩ **j** ⟨mows⟩
3 a teach **b** swim **c** helps **d** display
 e gobbles/wants

Week 7, Day 1
Pg 32

> Whales, dolphins, seals, and sea lions are ⟨marine mammals⟩.
>
> Mammals cannot breathe under water because they have lungs, not gills. They must come to the surface to breathe.
>
> The babies of whales and dolphins are born underwater. The mothers push the babies to the surface to take their first breath.
>
> Seals and sea lions spend most of their time in the water, feeding on fish, squid, and penguins. They also spend time on land, resting. Seal pups are born on land and like all marine mammal babies, they are fed on milk.

1 c, d, f   **2** a, d

Week 7, Day 2
Pg 33

> Many birds depend on the sea for their food. Wading birds, penguins, albatrosses, gulls, and pelicans hunt and eat ⟨fish and other sea creatures⟩.
>
> Wading birds, such as oystercatchers, live and feed along the shore. Long, spindly legs help them wade through shallow water. Their thin beaks dig around for small animals in the water and mud.
>
> Out over the deeper ocean, birds need to be able to fly for long periods of time. The albatross has very long wings so that it can glide for hours. It can stay in the air for weeks at a time. These seabirds dive into the water to catch their food.
>
> Penguins cannot fly at all. They use their flippers and their webbed feet to swim very fast and catch fish.

1 they both hunt and eat fish and other sea creatures
2 oystercatchers use their thin beaks to dig around for small animals in the water and mud; albatrosses dive into the water to catch food
3 an albatross has long wings so it can glide for hours; a penguin cannot fly at all

Week 7, Day 3
Pg 34

1 Check for correct spelling of each word.
2 a squirrel **b** syllable **c** crystal **d** battle
 e metal **f** satchel
3 a shuffle **b** metal /crystal **c** moral
 d battle **e** eagle
4 a crystal **b** wrinkle **c** handle **d** marble
 e beetle
5 a beetle **b** squirrel **c** handle **d** eagle

Week 7, Day 4
Pg 35

1 a squirrel **b** total **c** mammal
 d wrinkle **e** handle
2 Check for correct spelling of each word.
3 a article **b** rural **c** vertical
 d enamel **e** mineral **f** constable
 g resemble **h** scoundrel **i** grumble
 j morsel
4 a morsel **b** resemble **c** rural
 d vertical **e** enamel **f** article
 g constable

Week 7, Day 5
Pg 36

1 a will **b** was **c** am **d** are **e** have **f** does **g** is
2 a is **b** are **c** has **d** have **e** was **f** were
 g does **h** do
3 a are falling. **b** is ticking. **c** were training
4 a does **b** do

Week 8, Day 1
Pg 37

> Emperor penguins are the only warm-blooded animals that spend winter in Antarctica.
>
> In May, the ⟨female lays a single egg⟩ and then walks to the sea to feed. She stays at sea until the egg hatches.
>
> The male stays behind to look after the egg. He balances the egg on his feet and protects it under a thick roll of skin called a brood pouch. During this time, the male does not eat.
>
> The egg hatches after about two months. The chick stays in the brood pouch until it can survive on its own.
>
> The female returns to feed the chick. The male then leaves to find food.

1 c   **2** a   **3** d

Week 8, Day 2
Pg 38

> Caribou are wild reindeer. They live in the Arctic regions of Russia, Alaska, Canada, and Greenland.
>
> Caribou live in herds. The herd protects calves from predators such as bears, lynxes, and golden eagles.
>
> In ⟨spring⟩, caribou migrate about 3,000 miles north to breed on the Arctic tundra. All summer, they eat leaves and grass to build up their fat stores for winter.
>
> When the tundra becomes cold and windy, the herds migrate south to forests. They spend winter in forests, feeding on plants such as lichens and mosses.

1 in spring
2 a summer **b** winter **c** the tundra becomes cold and windy **d** winter **e** caribou migrate 3,000 miles north to breed on the Arctic tundra

Week 8, Day 3
Pg 39

1 Check for correct spelling of each word.
2 a sludge **b** dodge **c** fudge **d** ridge
 e ledge **f** judge **g** trudge **h** pledge
3 a trudge **b** nudge **c** lodge **d** ledge
 e large **f** strange **g** smudge **h** dodge
4 a bridge **b** fridge **c** badge

Week 8, Day 4
Pg 40

1 a frige fridge **b** doge dodge
 c juge judge **d** stagge stage
 e ledje ledge **f** pledje pledge
2 Check for correct spelling of each word.
3 a porridge **b** language **c** fidget
 d badger **e** cartridge **f** arrange
 g gadget **h** lodger
4 a cartridge **b** badger **c** gadget
 d fidget **e** lodger **f** average

Week 8, Day 5
Pg 41

1 a are planning **b** is coloring
 c was standing **d** were sitting
 e will be cheering
2 a She was drawing. **b** They were talking.
 c We were going. **d** You were trying.
 e It was shaking.
3 a is am/was **b** were was
 c were was **d** close closing
 e leave leaving **f** was were

Week 9, Day 1
Pg 42

> Glass is made by mixing sand, limestone, and soda ash in (a furnace) The molten glass is poured into a mold or laid out in sheets. It hardens as it cools.
>
> Glass breaks easily. This property can be changed by adding chemicals or by changing the way glass cools. If you reheat glass, then quickly cool it, the glass becomes much stronger.
>
> Pyrex glass is a special type of glass. It does not expand when it is heated as much as normal glass.
>
> Glass can be recycled over and over again.

1 c **2** b **3** d **4** a **5** a

Week 9, Day 2
Pg 43

> Most metals come from minerals. Rocks that contain minerals are called ores. They are (crushed) or (heated) to collect the metal.
>
> Iron comes from iron ore. It is made into steel by adding carbon.
>
> Metals can corrode. When rust eats away at iron or steel, it corrodes. Rust is a flaky, brown substance that forms when oxygen, water, and iron combine. This process is faster if the water is salty.
>
> An alloy is a mixture of metals. For example, stainless steel is an alloy of steel and chromium. Alloys have different properties. They can be stronger, lighter, and softer than other metals.

1 crushed and heated

2 because the text tells you rust eats away at iron or steel, and that process is faster in salty water

3 because steel is a metal, but stainless steel is an alloy, and alloys have different properties to pure metals

Week 9, Day 3
Pg 44

1 Check for correct spelling of each word.

2 a tanned **b** skinned **c** mapped **d** sipped
e gripped **f** begged **g** tugged **h** pinned

3 a quizzed **b** sipped **c** tugged **d** flipped
e knotted **f** begged **g** skipped **h** swapped

4 Missing letters are underlined
 a gripped **b** skipped **c** cropped
 d knotted **e** stemmed **f** tugged

5 a skipped **b** cropped **c** stemmed
 d knotted **e** spotted **f** mapped

Week 9, Day 4
Pg 45

1 a pined pinned **b** croped cropped
 c skiped skipped **d** maped mapped
 e troted trotted **f** fliped flipped

2 Check for correct spelling of each word.

3 a quipped **b** equipped **c** boycotted
 d omitted **e** shunned **f** throbbed
 g clogged **h** strapped **i** allotted
 j overlapped

4 a overlapped **b** allotted **c** throbbed
 d clogged **e** strapped **f** shunned

Week 9, Day 5
Pg 46

1 a Mom handed out backpacks, compasses, and maps.

b You can read a book, a magazine, or the newspaper.

c Sam can play the flute, the violin, and the piano.

d I put my towel, T-shirt, shorts, and socks into the laundry basket.

e The box contained a yellow ribbon, a silver buckle, and an old coin.

f I watered the plants, swept the drive, and took the dog for a walk.

2 ✓ c

3 a At the market, we bought bread, milk, and vegetables.

b Amazingly, he has never eaten pizza, pasta, hamburgers, or doughnuts.

c From the top of the building, we could see the sea, mountains, and farmland.

d Because I was sick I couldn't visit Grandma on Monday, Tuesday, or Wednesday.

4 a *Answers will vary. Suggested answer:* On Tuesday at the art store, we bought paint, pencils, and crayons.

b *Answers will vary. Suggested answer:* Mammals like whales, tigers, and rhinos all nurse their young.

REVIEW 1
Spelling

1 a taste **b** flute **c** threw **d** rescue

2 d **3** a **4** fridge

5 Missing letters are underlined
 a pearl **b** eerie **c** prairie

6 a sipped **b** spotted **c** grinning
 d whipping

7 gigantic

8 a battle **b** total **c** squirrel

Grammar

1 a beach Sunday **b** cousins Italy
 c train Houston **d** Jerome park

2 a Amazon, Nile **b** Japan, Tokyo
 c Grand Canyon, Arizona **d** July, August

3 child, powder, criminal
 power, crime, childhood

4 a The Cricket in Times Square
 b The Beginning of Everything

5 a them **b** They **c** it **d** themselves

6 a are, put **b** smiled, saw **c** has, follows

7 a are **b** was **c** am **d** were

8 a Dominic is collecting old coins.
 b Our dog was running around the garden.

9 a *Answers will vary. Suggested answer:* strawberries, raspberries, blueberries, and bananas.

b *Answers will vary. Suggested answer:* milk, cheese, flour, and ice cream.

Comprehension

1 c **2** d

3 *Answers will vary. Suggested answer:* The text says, "Samuel sat up in bed, his body tense, and listened intently." Being tense and listening intently are signs of being scared.

4 a **5** c **6** b **7** b

8 *Answers will vary. Suggested answer:* The hairs on Samuel's neck rose because the clicking sound was coming from his room. This tells the reader that he is worried and scared.

Week 10, Day 1
Pg 52

> I (hate) being a twin. I guess it might be OK if you were an identical twin. You could fool other people by pretending you were the other twin. But Sam and I only got the bad bits of being a twin—like having to share our birthday. That was a real drag.
>
> "I'm not having a party with all of his friends there," I yelled.
>
> "Now Fairlie," Mom began in her best 'don't-argue-with-me' voice, "I'm not having two separate birthday parties. I don't see why you make so much fuss about this."

1 c **2** b **3** a **4** c **5** d

Week 10, Day 2
Pg 53

> "Perhaps I should just organize a party for Sam this year," Mom threatened.
>
> "Yeah. Perhaps there should just be a party for Sam," Sam agreed.
>
> "Fine," I said. "Suits me. Sam can have his party this year and I'll have mine next year."
>
> Sam didn't look quite so happy with that idea. Mom did though.
>
> "What a wonderful idea, Fairlie," she said.
>
> "Wonderful," Sam said without enthusiasm.

1 she thought it was a wonderful idea

2 he was happy

3 he wasn't enthusiastic about taking turns

4 the phrase "without enthusiasm"

Week 10, Day 3
Pg 54

1 Check for correct spelling of each word.

2 a un **b** un **c** mis **d** un **e** dis
 f dis **g** un **h** un **i** un **j** dis
 k dis **l** un **m** mis **n** mis **o** mis
 p dis

3 a disregard **b** disorder **c** misfit
 d unlawful **e** dismount **f** mislaid
 g disloyal **h** unstable

4

un	mis	dis
unhappy	misfit	dislike
unclear	mislaid	dislodge
uneasy	mismatch	disown
unwilling	misunderstood	discount
unstable		disorder
unlawful		disregard
unchanged		disinfect
		disloyal
		dismount

Week 10, Day 4
Pg 55

1 a <u>disclear</u> unclear   **b** <u>mislike</u> dislike
   c <u>mischanged</u> unchanged
   d <u>unlayed</u> mislaid   **e** <u>misinfect</u> disinfect
   f <u>dishappy</u> unhappy   **g** <u>diswilling</u> unwilling
   h <u>disunderstood</u> misunderstood

2 Check for correct spelling of each word.

3 a disqualify   **b** uncommon
   c unsatisfactory   **d** unpopular
   e disadvantage   **f** discontented
   g disjointed   **h** discomfort
   i misfortune   **j** misadventure

4 a disadvantage   **b** disqualify   **c** uncommon
   d discomfort   **e** unpopular

Week 10, Day 5
Pg 56

1 a cute   **b** cotton   **c** black   **d** iron
   e wooden   **f** mountain   **g** old

2 a ugly red plastic   **b** beautiful pink silk
   c smart white cotton   **d** pretty green glass
   e comfortable old leather
   f unusual round wooden
   g horrible yellow metal

3 a silver, sharp, curved, steel
   b fast, strong, wild, spotted

Week 11, Day 1
Pg 57

> Toby climbed down the stairs to the beach. He looked out across the sea as he walked. Suddenly, Toby tripped over something and fell face first into the sand.
> Toby stood up and brushed the wet sand from his clothes. He bent down for a closer look at what he had tripped on.
> It was a piece of wood. As Toby lifted it, something underneath caught his eye. He dug through the sand and uncovered a bell. Toby lifted the bell and scraped off the barnacles. There was a date carved on its side.
> "1892," Toby read.

1 d   **2** a   **3** b   **4** b   **5** c

Week 11, Day 2
Pg 58

> Felix Thompson was seated at the table.
> Felix stood and looked at Toby. "I'm sorry about before." Then he handed Toby a black book. "This is my great-grandfather's diary. It tells all about the night of October 12, 1892."
> Toby was stunned. He opened the lighthouse keeper's diary and read. "It has been a bad week. Storm, after storm, after storm. I was dead on my feet. Fell asleep on watch. The light must have gone out during the night. I didn't know any damage had been done until the next day. When I heard that *The Isabella* was missing in my waters, I lied when I filled in the logbook."

1 he was tired because it had been a bad week of storms

2 a ship called *The Isabella* went missing near his lighthouse

3 he didn't want to get into trouble

Week 11, Day 3
Pg 59

1 Check for correct spelling of each word.

2 a donkeys   **b** groceries

3 a donkeys   **b** replies   **c** centuries
   d remedies   **e** kidneys   **f** diaries
   g displays   **h** chimneys

4 a groceries   **b** memories   **c** donkeys
   d holidays   **e** chimneys   **f** remedies

Week 11, Day 4
Pg 60

1 Missing letters are <u>underlined</u>
   a entr<u>ies</u>   **b** repl<u>ays</u>   **c** suppl<u>ies</u>
   d displ<u>ays</u>   **e** worr<u>ies</u>   **f** industr<u>ies</u>
   g holid<u>ays</u>

2 a industries   **b** centuries   **c** chimneys
   d groceries   **e** factories   **f** displays
   g remedies

3 Check for correct spelling of each word.

4 a pulleys   **b** abbeys   **c** ceremonies
   d mysteries   **e** societies   **f** convoys

5 a categories   **b** pulleys   **c** ceremonies
   d societies   **e** strategies

Week 11, Day 5
Pg 61

1 a where   **b** how   **c** when   **d** how
   e how often   **f** where   **g** when

2 a neatly, hurriedly, easily
   b tomorrow, now, earlier
   c always, sometimes, daily
   d nearby, there, somewhere

3 a always   **b** away   **c** rapidly
   d correctly   **e** nowhere   **f** tonight

Week 12, Day 1
Pg 62

> Two old crows sat on a fence rail.
> Two old crows sat on a fence rail,
> Thinking of effect and cause,
> Of weeds and flowers,
> And nature's laws.
> One of them muttered, one of them stuttered,
> One of them stuttered, one of them muttered.
> Each of them thought far more than he uttered.
> One crow asked the other crow a riddle.
> One crow asked the other crow a riddle:
> The muttering crow
> Asked the stuttering crow,
> "Why does a bee have a sword to his fiddle?"

1 b   **2** d   **3** a

Week 12, Day 2
Pg 63

> "Why does a bee have a sword to his fiddle?"
> "Bee-cause," said the other crow,
> "Bee-cause,
> B B B B B B B B B B B B B B B B-cause."
> Just then a bee flew close to their rail. -
> "Buzzzzzzzzzzzzzzzzzzz   zzzzzzzzz zzzzzzzzzzzzzzzz   ZZZZZZZZ."
> And those two black crows
> Turned pale,
> And away those crows did sail.
> Why?
> B B B B B B B B B B B B B B-cause.
> B B B B B B B B B B B B B B B-cause.
> "Buzzzzzzzzzzzzzzzzzzz   zzzzzzzzz
> Zzzzzzzzzzzzzzzz   ZZZZZZZZ."

1 a rail
   b "Buzzzzzzzzzzzzzzzzzzz zzzzzzzzz zzzzzzzzzzzzzzzz ZZZZZZZZ."
   c the two black crows turned pale
   d they flew away

Week 12, Day 3
Pg 64

1 Check for correct spelling of each word.

2 a ice: notice, office, justice, advice, police, device, practice, hospice, novice, prejudice, solstice
   b ise: advise, promise, surprise, exercise, supervise, advertise
   c realize, organize

3 a novice   **b** prejudice   **c** supervise
   d practice   **e** precise   **f** advise

Week 12, Day 4
Pg 65

1 a exercise   **b** organize   **c** advertise
   d notice   **e** promise   **f** precise
   g supervise

2 Check for correct spelling of each word.

3 a edifice   **b** precipice   **c** accomplice
   d cowardice   **e** criticize   **f** apprentice
   g lattice   **h** emphasize

4 a lattice   **b** visualize   **c** emphasize
   d accomplice   **e** apprentice   **f** criticize

Week 12, Day 5
Pg 66

1 a comfortable   **b** comfortably
   c cruelly   **d** cruel   **e** easy   **f** easily

2 a <u>softly</u> soft   **b** <u>cautious</u> cautiously
   c <u>loud</u> loudly   **d** <u>honestly</u> honest
   e <u>enormously</u> enormous   **f** <u>wise</u> wisely

3 a adjective   **b** adverb   **c** adverb
   d adjective   **e** adverb   **f** adjective
   g adjective   **h** adverb

Week 13, Day 1
Pg 67

> There were once two brothers who were very different from each other. The older brother, though rich, always wanted more. The younger brother was not rich, but he was happy with what he had.
> One day the younger brother found a sparrow with a broken wing. He took it home and nursed it back to health. When it was time for the sparrow to fly away, it said, "You showed me great kindness, yet expected nothing in return. Please take this pumpkin seed. Plant it in your garden and wait for it to ripen."
> When the pumpkins ripened, they contained gold, silver, and diamonds.

1 a   **2** c   **3** b, d   **4** b

Week 13, Day 2
Pg 68

> News of his brother's sudden fortune reached the older brother. When he heard what had happened, he took out a slingshot, shot a sparrow and broke its wing. He took the bird home and nursed it while thinking, "The sooner you are better, the sooner I get my reward."
>
> When the bird was better, it gave the older brother a pumpkin seed. The seed sprouted into a vine, but the vine did not grow along the ground—it grew up into the sky. "I shall climb the vine and collect my reward," said the older brother.
>
> He climbed the vine all the way to the moon. As soon as he stepped onto the moon, the vine disappeared.

1 he thought once the bird was back to health he would be given a reward

2 *Answers will vary. Suggested answer:* The sparrow would have felt victim to the cruel older brother. The sparrow wanted revenge for the cruelty.

3 *Answers will vary. Ask children to talk through responses.*

Week 13, Day 3
Pg 69

1 Check for correct spelling of each word.

3 a smaller **b** stronger **c** earlier
d faster **e** shorter **f** warmest
g quieter **h** happiest **i** broadest
j youngest

3 a shorter **b** happiest

4

fast	faster	fastest
early	earlier	earliest
happy	happier	happiest
short	shorter	shortest
proud	prouder	proudest
strong	stronger	strongest

Week 13, Day 4
Pg 70

1 a broader, broadest **b** angrier, angriest
c fancier, fanciest **d** uglier, ugliest
e lazier, laziest **f** faster, fastest

2 Check for correct spelling of each word.

3 a lonelier **b** clumsier **c** scrawniest
d liveliest **e** looser **f** straightest
g stickier **h** glossiest **i** drearier
j greasiest

4 a glossiest **b** greasiest **c** looser
d stickier **e** straightest **f** drearier
g scrawniest

Week 13, Day 5
Pg 71

1 a an **b** my **c** these **d** their
e this **f** Some **g** many

2 a four **b** an **c** that **d** my

3 a fifth five **b** that those **c** three third
d an a **e** any many **f** much some
g a an

Week 14, Day 1
Pg 72

> Research stations in Antarctica are busy places. A visitor might describe a typical day like this:
>
> Early this morning I joined a group of meteorologists as they launched a weather balloon. The balloon rose high into the sky and recorded temperature, wind speed, and air pressure. Scientists then studied the results.
>
> After that, I watched a glaciologist drill ice cores. Ice cores contain air bubbles of gas from thousands of years ago. Glaciologists studied the ice cores to learn more about the Earth's atmosphere.

1 c **2** b **3** a **4** d **5** b

Week 14, Day 2
Pg 73

> Research stations in Antarctica are busy places. A visitor might describe a typical afternoon like this:
>
> After lunch, I flew by helicopter to where geologists were collecting rock samples. These contain important information about the Earth from millions of years ago.
>
> Finally, I saw a marine biologist check the electronic tag that was glued to a Weddell seal. These tags record information about where marine animals travel in the ocean.

1 collecting rock samples

2 important information about Earth from millions of years ago

3 *Answers will vary. Suggested answer:* a geologist collects and studies rock samples to collect important information about Earth from millions of years ago

4 *Answers will vary. Suggested answer:* an animal that lives in the sea or ocean

Week 14, Day 3
Pg 74

1 Check for correct spelling of each word.

2 a chief, field, piece, priest, shield, brief, friend, fierce, patient, mischief, grieve, shriek, believe
b ceiling, veil, their, receive, deceit, heir, either

3 a priest **b** shield

4 a mischief **b** chief **c** patient **d** heir
e shield **f** veil

Week 14, Day 4
Pg 75

1 a beleive believe **b** deciet deceit
c shreik shriek **d** feild field
e viel veil **f** Thier Their
g freind friend **h** sheild shield

2 Check for correct spelling of each word.

3 a achieve **b** protein **c** siege
d yield/achieve

4 a seize **b** weird **c** feisty **d** leisure

Week 14, Day 5
Pg 76

1 a on **b** at **c** some **d** an/from **e** seventh/of

2 a with the wobbly legs **b** from our orchard
c on the corner **d** in the jungle
e around the collar

3 a balls **b** book **c** boy **d** bed

Week 15, Day 1
Pg 77

> The most common way to make electricity is to burn a fuel, such as coal. This heats water to make steam. The steam spins a turbine. This powers a generator to make electricity.
>
> There are other ways to make electricity. Wind and water can also power a generator. A solar cell absorbs sunlight to make electricity.
>
> Electrical energy can be converted into other forms of energy, such as heat, light, and sound.
>
> Lightning is an electrical current that jumps through the air. The current heats the air hotter than the surface of the Sun.

1 b **2** b, c, e

Week 15, Day 2
Pg 78

> Work waiting to be done is potential energy. Work being done is kinetic energy.
>
> Potential energy is energy that could be released or used. A coiled spring has potential energy because the spring could uncoil. A rock on the edge of a cliff has potential energy. Its potential energy is the energy that would be released if it fell from the cliff.
>
> The food we eat becomes potential energy when it is stored in our bodies. When this energy is used to do things, such as kick a ball, it becomes kinetic energy.

1 potential energy

2 a definition of potential energy so readers know that it's "work waiting to be done"
b example of potential energy in objects like coiled springs and a rock on the edge of a cliff
c example of potential energy in the food we eat that is stored for later activities

Week 15, Day 3
Pg 79

1 Check for correct spelling of each word.

2 a finally **b** gently **c** honestly **d** promptly
e sharply **f** personally **g** firstly

3 a honestly **b** secondly **c** rapidly **d** terribly
e personally **f** briskly **g** gently **h** finally

4 Missing letters are underlined
a briskly **b** truly **c** instantly **d** roughly
e normally **f** slightly **g** sharply

5 a personally **b** publicly **c** honestly
d secondly **e** normally **f** similarly
g promptly

Week 15, Day 4
Pg 80

1 a briskly, finally **b** firstly, secondly
c honestly, publicly **d** truly, rapidly
e Normally, promptly

2 Check for correct spelling of each word.

3 a eventually **b** necessarily **c** vaguely
d apparently **e** obviously **f** actually
g gradually **h** desperately **i** conveniently
j generally

4 a obviously **b** eventually **c** generally
d gradually **e** desperately

Week 15, Day 5
Pg 81

1 a to, with   **b** of, over   **c** in, on
   d by, about   **e** at, through   **f** into, across
   g along, beside

2 a from **b** under **c** of **d** into **e** down **f** behind

3 circle: on, of, of

Week 16, Day 1
Pg 82

> The countries that make up the Arctic often argue about who owns it. Many countries <u>want the Arctic's valuable oil and gas deposits.</u>
>
> In 2007, 50 Russian scientists used a mini submarine to research the seabed under the North Pole. They were trying to prove that the land underneath the Arctic Ocean is connected to their land in Siberia. They even planted a Russian flag on the seabed.
>
> There are over 10 billion tons of oil and natural gas deposits in the Arctic territory. Canada, Norway, and Greenland are also trying to prove that they own the land under the Arctic waters.

1 b   **2** d   **3** a

Week 16, Day 2
Pg 83

> An igloo is a <u>dome-shaped shelter, made out of blocks of snow.</u>
> **What you need:**
> • A snow saw   • Dry snow
> **What to do:**
> 1. Use the saw to cut blocks of hard, dry snow, about one yard long and 40 inches deep.
> 2. Draw a circle in the snow and stand in the middle of it. Place the blocks around the circle in layers. The blocks of snow should overlap and lean towards the center.
> 3. Place the last block on top of the igloo. Cut it to fit the hole.
> 4. Cut a tunnel under the wall for the entrance. Poke small breathing holes in the walls.

1 to inform how to make an igloo

2 use, draw, stand, place, cut, poke

3 somebody living in the snow

4 *Answers will vary. Ask children to talk through responses.*

5 *Answers will vary. Ask children to talk through responses.*

Week 16, Day 3
Pg 84

1 Check for correct spelling of each word.

2 a yolk   **b** throne   **c** fowl   **d** maze

3 Missing letters are <u>underlined</u>
   a <u>lesson</u>   **b** <u>through</u>   **c** <u>fought</u>   **d** <u>scene</u>
   e <u>throne</u>   **f** <u>fowl</u>   **g** <u>tide</u>   **h** <u>maize</u>

4 a yoke   **b** maize   **c** bawl   **d** maze
   e fowl   **f** lessen   **g** fort

Week 16, Day 4
Pg 85

1 a fowl, foul **b** fought, fort   **c** maize, maze
   d threw, through   **e** thrown, throne
   f tied, tide   **g** bawl, ball

2 Check for correct spelling of each word.

3 a weather **b** cruise   **c** guest **d** accept
   e except   **f** crews   **g** affect **h** effect

4 a cruise   **b** whether **c** effect   **d** guessed
   e weather **f** affect

Week 16, Day 5
Pg 86

1 a on   **b** at   **c** in   **d** from   **e** with, of
2 a by   **b** with   **c** in, on   **d** of, from
   e to   **f** near   **g** around

3 check: a, b, d, e, h

Week 17, Day 1
Pg 87

> It's summer—let us mow your lawn! Our fast, on time lawn mowing service always does a great job! Long list of happy customers, who enjoy professional work with a smile. Free quotes based on the size of your lawn, how many trees in it, and how overgrown it is for the first mow. We also do yard cleanups, weed removal, and gutter clearing. No job too big or small.

1 *Answers will vary. Ask children to talk through responses.*

Week 17, Day 2
Pg 88

> Saturday morning in my house means CARTOONS. Old cartoons, new cartoons, action cartoons, funny cartoons. Cartoon kids, cartoon cats, cartoon squids, and cartoon rats. Cartoon goodies being saved, cartoon baddies being blamed. Cartoon squirrels in a cage, cartoon aliens in a rage.
> But I refuse to watch unless I get my bowl of Corny-Biks. Because cartoons aren't cartoons without Corny-Biks.

1 *Answers will vary. Ask children to talk through responses.*

Week 17, Day 3
Pg 89

1 Check for correct spelling of each word.

2 a present, parent, silent, talent, recent, absent, student, continent, frequent, dependent, confident
   b distant, servant, infant, vacant, important, merchant, pleasant, elephant, contestant

3 a silent   **b** vacant   **c** important
   d continent   **e** student

4 a present **b** infant **c** elephant **d** student

Week 17, Day 4
Pg 90

1 a distant   **b** absent   **c** talent
   d merchant **e** elephant **f** continent

2 Check for correct spelling of each word.

3 a assistant **b** hesitant   **c** different
   d arrogant **e** president **f** ignorant

4 a fragrant **b** hesitant   **c** ignorant
   d innocent **e** different **f** arrogant
   g permanent

Week 17, Day 5
Pg 91

1 a After a while, the children started to get bored.
   b Silently, the tiger stalked its prey.
   c Without a word, he left the room.
   d Behind the clouds, the sun is still shining.
   e Quickly, the ballerinas took their places.
   f In a few minutes, the storm will be over.

2 a Without any hesitation, she ran to help the little boy.
   b By 7 o'clock, he had finished his breakfast.
   c With a spring in her step, she crossed the road.
   d In a little while, we will know the results.
   e Beside the river, there are lots of shady trees.

3 a *Answers will vary. Suggested answer:* Outside my house, the moon shone brightly in the sky.
   b *Answers will vary. Suggested answer:* In the middle of the night, the children snuck down to the kitchen for a midnight snack.

Week 18, Day 1
Pg 92

> Screws hold things together, and lower and raise things.
> A screw is an inclined plane wrapped around a cylinder. The inclined plane forms a ridge along the cylinder. This ridge is called the thread of the screw.
> As a screw is turned by a screwdriver, it turns a greater distance than it moves forward. The turning motion becomes a forward motion.
> A Greek mathematician called Archimedes invented a screw machine more than 2,200 years ago. It was used to lift water into fields and out of ships.

1 a, e, f

2 *Answers will vary. Ask children to talk through responses.*

Week 18, Day 2
Pg 93

> A wheel with a rod, called an axle, through its center can lift and move loads.
> The axle is joined to the wheel. When either the wheel or axle turns, the other part also turns. The steering wheel in a car is a wheel and axle.
> The circle turned by a wheel is much larger than the circle turned by the axle. The longer distance turned by the wheel makes the axle turn more powerfully.
> A wheel and axle is often used with gears. A gear is a wheel with cogs around its edge. Several gears can be connected, so that their cogs lock into each other.

1 A wheel with a rod, called an axle, through its centre can lift and move loads.

2 The circle turned by a wheel is much larger than the circle turned by the axle.

3 The steering wheel in a car is a wheel and axle. A wheel and axle is often used with gears.

Week 18, Day 3
Pg 94

1 Check for correct spelling of each word.

2 a dragonfly   **b** fingerprint **c** necklace
   d staircase

3 a suitcase /staircase   **b** dragonfly
   c sometimes   **d** seashore   **e** password
   f underground **g** forehead   **h** handcuff

4 a fingerprint   **b** bookstore   **c** necklace
   d playground   **e** suitcase   **f** password
   g underground **h** dishwasher

Week 18, Day 4
Pg 95
1 a sunbathe **b** forehead **c** footstep
d meanwhile **e** sometimes
2 a footstep **b** dishwasher **c** fingerprint
d backstage **e** horseback **f** bookstore
3 Check for correct spelling of each word.
4 a granddaughter **b** peppermint
c keyboard **d** firefighter **e** hairdresser
f saucepan **g** weatherman **h** toothpaste
i flashlight **j** earthworm
5 a flashlight **b** earthworm **c** toothpaste
d silkworm **e** saucepan **f** firefighter
g peppermint

Week 18, Day 5
Pg 96
1

Contractions	Possessive nouns
that's mine	baby's bottle
isn't yours	donkey's ears
I'm six	boy's bike
I've finished	bird's nest
you'll need	cyclist's helmet
we're leaving	

2 a friend's/sister's **b** dog's
c friend's/sister's **d** man's
3 a pig's **b** sister's **c** Henry's **d** boy's

REVIEW 2
Spelling
1 a bravest **b** foul **c** faster **d** shortest
2 c **3** b
4 Missing letters are underlined
a rec<u>ei</u>ve **b** th<u>ei</u>r **c** misch<u>ie</u>f **d** p<u>ie</u>ce
5 personally
6 Missing letters are underlined
a promi<u>se</u> **b** organi<u>ze</u> **c** prejud<u>ice</u>
d surpr<u>ise</u>
7 a handcuff **b** suitcase
Grammar
1 a My friend has a fluffy white Persian kitten.
b We spotted three large African elephants in the distance.
2 a how **b** when **c** where **d** how
3 a (careful)/adjective **b** (Carefully)/adverb
c (easily)/adverb
4 a (an) **b** (those) **c** (this) **d** (its)
5 a a flock of birds
b the stone bench beneath the old oak tree
6 a beside **b** around **c** for **d** under
e about **f** through
7 a at dawn and dusk **b** with their paws
c in thick, tropical jungles
d on their coats
8 a At 6 o'clock every morning, my alarm wakes me up.
b In the distance, I could see a herd of elephants.
c Carefully, the children removed the weeds.
9 a I think the cat's toy is under one of those chairs
b The ducklings followed their mother to the water's edge.

Comprehension
1 b **2** c
3 *Answers will vary. Suggested answer:*
The text says that "time keeping became much more accurate" and this tells us that later clocks told the time more precisely.
4 c **5** c **6** b **7** c
8 The text tells us the watch got its name because early watches had to be watched to see when they struck the hour.

Week 19, Day 1
Pg 102

> Kevin could see the echidna so clearly—its black-tipped, creamy quills, as sharp as knitting needles; the coarse, black hairs on its face, like bristles on a brush; its eyes two beads shining against the dull blackness of its snout.

1 a, d **2** a, d **3** c **4** d **5** a

Week 19, Day 2
Pg 103

> Kevin climbed to the highest branch of the tree and balanced there. His legs had turned to (stone), but he forced himself to look down. Brown leaves were floating on the murky water, like little boats. He took a deep breath and plunged into the pool. It wasn't the greatest dive he had ever done, but as he surfaced, the fear was gone.

1 metaphor
2 *Answers will vary. Suggested answer:*
Kevin's legs feel heavy and he feels like it is hard for him to take action and dive in
3 *Answers will vary. Ask children to talk through responses.*
4 simile
5 *Answers will vary. Ask children to talk through responses.*

Week 19, Day 3
Pg 104
1 Check for correct spelling of each word.
2

say	said
stick	stuck
write	wrote
ride	ridden
drive	driven
pay	paid
hurt	hurt
string	strung

3 a swung **b** slunk **c** strode **d** stuck
e strung **f** paid **g** flown **h** sprang
4 Missing letters are underlined
a w<u>ept</u> **b** r<u>idden</u> **c** p<u>aid</u> **d** fl<u>ew</u>
e h<u>urt</u> **f** dr<u>ove</u> **g** sw<u>ung</u> **h** w<u>ritten</u>
i str<u>ode</u> **j** sl<u>unk</u> **k** sw<u>ore</u>/sw<u>ung</u>
l s<u>aid</u>
5 a written **b** ridden **c** strung
d beaten **e** forgiven

Week 19, Day 4
Pg 105
1 a <u>fly</u> flew **b** <u>write</u> written **c** <u>fly</u> flown
d <u>pay</u> paid **e** <u>drive</u> driven **f** <u>say</u> said
g <u>ride</u> ridden
2 Check for correct spelling of each word.
3 a foretold/foresaw **b** taught
c interwoven **d** outgrown **e** withdrew
f overheard **g** understood **h** foresaw
4 a overheard **b** understood **c** interwoven
d outgrown **e** taught

Week 19, Day 5
Pg 106
1 a (simon) (my) **b** (whose) (is)
c (put) **d** (zack) (have) (my)
e (the) **f** (you) (the) **g** (the)
2 Check: a, d, f
3 *Answers will vary. Suggested answer:*
"The soup is very hot," said Mom, "so let's leave it to cool for a few minutes before sitting down to eat."

Week 20, Day 1
Pg 107

> "If I win the map-a-thon," said Lisa, "I don't want to take Samantha to Wonderland. I want to take Sarah." Sarah is her best friend.
>
> I couldn't believe that Lisa wouldn't want to take me. She knew how much I wanted to go to Wonderland. I didn't keep it a secret.
>
> "You're the meanest person I know!" I told her. "It would serve you right if someone else won the tickets to Wonderland."
>
> I decided I would do my best to try to win. Then I'd take one of my friends instead of Lisa.
>
> I grabbed her atlas and went to my bedroom to study.

1 c **2** d **3** c **4** a

Week 20, Day 2
Pg 108

> When Ram saw me, he stopped shouting. I hid behind Buzz, trying to make myself as small as possible.
> Ram (frowned.) He loomed over Buzz. "Do you know the penalty for bringing an outsider into the computer?" he (roared.)
> Buzz nodded. "But I was hoping you would see this as a special case," Buzz said, "and show a little kindness to a poor girl who needs the help of your great wisdom."
> Ram stopped frowning and began to smile a little Buzz told Ram about the map-a-thon and the trouble that I'd been having. I needed something to help me remember the names of countries, and cities, and especially of oceans and seas.

1 *Answers will vary. Ask children to talk through responses.*
2 frowned and roared
3 Buzz flattered Ram by talking about his greatness
4 *Answers will vary. Ask children to talk through responses.*

Week 20, Day 3
Pg 109

1 Check for correct spelling of each word.

2 a color, harbor, rumor, labor, favor, odor, humor, honor, janitor

b nature, injure, picture, mixture, capture, fracture, scripture, adventure, treasure, puncture, structure

3 a treasure **b** harbor

4 a harbor **b** favor **c** adventure **d** puncture **e** nature **f** odor

Week 20, Day 4
Pg 110

1 a punctour puncture **b** mixtour mixture **c** adventour adventure **d** treasour treasure **e** pictour picture **f** harbure harbor **g** structour structure

2 Check for correct spelling of each word.

3 a curvature **b** pressure **c** enclosure **d** manufacture **e** signature **f** behavior **g** architecture **h** literature **i** procedure **j** savior

4 a savior **b** literature **c** signature **d** manufacture **e** architecture

Week 20, Day 5
Pg 111

1 a breathe, breath **b** threw, through **c** quite, quiet **d** wood, would **e** tied, tide

2 a like a rabbit

b something that grows on your head

c used to make bread

d the colored part of a plant

e a digit on your foot

f to pull

g to listen

h in this place

i belonging to them

j in that place

3 a won one **b** there their **c** sore saw **d** fore four **e** wear where **f** no know

Week 21, Day 1
Pg 112

> At home, Sam looked at the kitchen clock. One hour to go. Part of him was excited but the rest of him was terrified. What if they did something really bad to him? Something where they didn't mean to hurt him, but it went wrong?
>
> Sam knew there was no way out of it. He had to show up. He just wished that Tristan was coming too. He felt rotten about keeping it all from his friend. How was he going to tell Tristan if he did get into the Creaky House Club?
>
> "I'll see you later, Dad," Sam called, as he left the house and cycled towards The Creaky House.

1 b **2** d **3** c **4** c

Week 21, Day 2
Pg 113

> A voice that sounded familiar said, "Welcome to The Creaky House Club, Sam. As you know, we select our members very carefully. Firstly, we'd like to know why you want to join our club?"
>
> Sam had thought they'd ask him this question, but he still didn't have a good answer.
>
> "Well ... I'm a good basketball player and I'd like to be part of the most popular group in school at the moment," said Sam.
>
> "At the moment?" came the reply. "What do you mean 'at the moment'?"
>
> "I've goofed already," Sam thought. But aloud he said, "Well, at the moment and in the future I mean."

1 members of The Creaky House Club

2 the dialogue is informal so the text is likely to be a narrative for children aged 8–12 years

3 to entertain young people

4 *Answers will vary. Ask children to talk through responses.*

Week 21, Day 3
Pg 114

1 Check for correct spelling of each word.

2 a sphere **b** spaghetti

3 Missing letters are underlined

a whiskers **b** whilst **c** whine **d** whack **e** ghostly **f** phrase **g** whim **h** whiff **i** whereas **j** sphere **k** hyphen **l** pamphlet **m** which **n** spaghetti **o** whisk **p** graphic **q** pharmacy **r** whinny **s** alphabet **t** orphan

3

wh		gh	ph
which	whinny	ghostly	phrase
whim	whereas	spaghetti	sphere
whiff			pamphlet
whisk			pharmacy
whack			orphan
whine			hyphen
whilst			alphabet
whiskers			graphic

Week 21, Day 4
Pg 115

1 a whinny **b** alphabet **c** spaghetti **d** sphere **e** whisk **f** pharmacy **g** orphan

2 Check for correct spelling of each word.

3 a apostrophe **b** aghast **c** biography **d** sapphire **e** overwhelm **f** atmosphere **g** phoenix **h** phlegm **i** prophet

4 a worthwhile **b** atmosphere **c** phoenix **d** phlegm **e** sapphire

Week 21, Day 5
Pg 116

1 Check: b, c, d, e, i, j, l

2 a he **b** they **c** she **d** his

3 a Dad told the children that it was time to go home.

b The man asked us when we were leaving.

Week 22, Day 1
Pg 117

> **Narrator:** Once upon a time, there lived a young woman called Miya. Her father was lord of his people. One day, Miya was swimming in the river when she heard a voice.
>
> **Miya:** What was that? Who's there?
>
> **Narrator:** The voice said it would lead her to the man of her dreams, if she followed it.
>
> **Miya:** The man of my dreams! I would love to be married to him!
>
> **Narrator:** So Miya followed the voice as best she could through the jungle until she reached a cave.

1 b **2** d **3** a **4** b

Week 22, Day 2
Pg 118

> **Narrator:** One day Jose, a farmer from Miya's village, appeared at the cave.
>
> **Jose:** Miya? Miya? Are you there? There is a famine and we have no food. We are starving. Help us!
>
> **Miya:** <*to Lord of the Bats*> My husband, I love you but I must leave and return to my village. The villagers need me.
>
> **Narrator:** So Miya and Jose returned to their village, but Miya did not receive a hero's welcome.
>
> **Miya's father:** Stop right there! We are hungry because of you, Miya. It is your fault we have no corn.
>
> **Narrator:** Miya was very upset and returned to the Lord of the Bats.
>
> **Lord of the Bats:** Don't cry, Miya, because you can still help your village. This is what you must do.

1 *Answers will vary. Suggested answer:* Miya is kind and thinks of others—she leaves her husband to go and help the villagers

2 the Lord of the Bats is kind and understanding, for example where he says, "Don't cry, Miya, because you can still help your village". He formulates a new plan to help the villagers overcome the famine

Week 22, Day 3
Pg 119

1 Check for correct spelling of each word.

2 a mystery **b** gymnastics **c** hymn **d** oxygen **e** system **f** syllable **g** symbol **h** crystal **i** lyric

3 a gymnastics **b** pyramid **c** myth **d** crystal **e** oxygen **f** cygnet **g** hymn **h** mystery

4 a cygnet **b** myth **c** symptom **d** pyramid **e** bicycle **f** gym

Week 22, Day 4
Pg 120

1 a oxiygen oxygen **b** lyrik lyric **c** piramid pyramid **d** gim gym **e** cristal crystal **f** mysterie mystery **g** symptome symptom **h** Egypte Egypt

2 Check for correct spelling of each word.

3 a symphony **b** crypt **c** antonym **d** cymbal **e** hypnotize **f** cryptic **g** calypso **h** hypocrite

4 a cymbal **b** crypt **c** antonym **d** symbolic

Week 22, Day 5
Pg 121

1 a "Faster, Higher, Stronger"
  b "Earth Matters."   c "with lots of books."
  d "Life itself is the most wonderful fairy tale."
  e "Fall seven times, stand up eight"

2 a Our quote of the day is, "Today a reader, tomorrow a leader."
  b One of my favorite quotes from Dr. Seuss is, "You can find magic wherever you look."
  c "The sun does arise," is the first line of a poem by William Blake.
  d When Joe shouted, "Watch out!" everyone ducked.
  e The last thing his grandson said was, "When will I see you again?"

3 a Thomas Edison, inventor of the light bulb, said of his achievements, "I never did a day's work in my life. It was all fun."
  b The United Nations Convention on the Rights of the Child states that, "Children have the right to an education."
  c When I asked Mom what it was like to have the best daughter in the world, she said, "I don't know, dear. You'll have to ask Grandma."

Week 23, Day 1
Pg 122

Lion King wondered which animal could teach the Lion Prince. He wondered if Fox could do it. Fox, though clever, was a great liar and liars always cause trouble. He wondered about Mole. Mole was orderly and careful but never looked far ahead. The King wondered about Panther. Panther was strong, brave, and a great fighter, but liked fighting a little too much. The Lion knew that a good king is just, wise, and can solve things without fighting.

1 a, b, d   2 b, d, f

Week 23, Day 2
Pg 123

Lion was still thinking when Eagle flew by. "Of course!" Lion cried. "Eagle!" The Lion King sent his son to study at Eagle's court.

Years later, Lion Prince returned to his father, in time to take over his kingdom.

"Father," said the Lion Prince, "I have learned many things. I can tell where every bird can find water. I know what kind of food each bird needs. I know how many eggs it lays and the wants of every bird that flies. When I am in charge of the kingdom, I shall begin to teach our animals how to build nests."

The animals in the King's court howled with laughter. The King realized the Lion Prince had not been taught the knowledge a great king needs most of all—a knowledge of the wants and needs of his own people and land.

1 a where every bird can find water
  b what kind of food each bird needs
  c how many eggs each bird lays
  d the wants of every bird that flies

2 the wants and needs of his own people and land, so he could build a strong and happy kingdom

Week 23, Day 3
Pg 124

1 Check for correct spelling of each word.

2 a cheetah   b archery

3 a chemist   b enchant   c chapter   d hatchet
  e bleach   f archery   g chuckle   h chef
  i chubby   j chorus

4 a chord   b echo   c chapter   d bleach
  e enchant   f chorus

Week 23, Day 4
Pg 125

1 a coach, echo   b enchant, chord
  c cheetah, chunk   d choose, archery
  e Christmas, chore

2 Check for correct spelling of each word.

3 a chasm   b anchor   c chronicle
  d chandelier   e chivalry   f chocolate

4 a chocolate   b parachute   c choir
  d chasm   e chaos   f chronicle
  g chandelier

Week 23, Day 5
Pg 126

1 a certainty   b certainty   c possibility
  d certainty   e possibility   f certainty
  g possibility

2 a may/might   b will/must   c can't/won't
  d must   e might/may, can't

3 a might   b must   c won't   d may

Week 24, Day 1
Pg 127

Forces cause earthquakes, wind, and waves in and on the Earth.

The Earth's surface is made up of large, slow-moving plates of rock. The plates push against each other and pull apart. This releases energy, which causes the land above the plates to move. This might be an earth tremor that you can't feel or a violent earthquake.

Wind is caused by changes in air pressure. When warm air rises, cooler, heavier air rushes in to fill the space. This moving air is called wind.

Ocean waves are caused by the force of the wind.

1 b   2 c   3 a   4 d

Week 24, Day 2
Pg 128

When a basketball player shoots, a push force sends the ball toward the net. Friction with the air slows the ball down. Gravity pulls it back toward the court. The ball would just keep going up without the action of these forces.

An aircraft has four forces acting on it. The engines produce a forward force, called thrust. The wings produce an upward force called lift. Friction from air rushing over the aircraft, called drag, slows it down. Gravity pulls it toward the earth.

What happens to an object depends on the sum of all the forces acting on it. The basketball reaches the net because the force of the shot is greater than the effects of gravity and friction. The aircraft moves forward because the thrust from the engines is greater than gravity and drag.

1 friction

2 gravity pulls both down to Earth

3 a the force of the shot is greater than the effects of gravity and friction
  b the thrust from the engines is greater than gravity and drag

Week 24, Day 3
Pg 129

1 Check for correct spelling of each word.

2 a violin   b mountain

3 a robin   b pumpkin   c famine   d dolphin
  e vitamin   f villain   g bargain   h curtain
  i engine   j imagine

4	in	ine	ain
cousin	pumpkin	engine	mountain
dolphin	napkin	famine	captain
raisin	margin	imagine	certain
basin			curtain
robin			bargain
cabin			villain
violin			
vitamin			

Week 24, Day 4
Pg 130

1 a dolphin   b famine   c villain
  d engine   e raisin   f robin

2 Check for correct spelling of each word.

3 a penguin   b porcelain   c feminine
  d javelin   e examine   f chieftain
  g medicine   h origin

4 a examine   b medicine   c chieftain
  d discipline   e javelin   f origin

Week 24, Day 5
Pg 131

1 a The plumber   b Their new car
  c This little key   d My friends
  e My brother and I

2 a The bees are collecting pollen from the flowers.
  b The very hungry caterpillar ate everything in sight.
  c The largest building on the street is the post office.
  d A few children in my ballet class are going to the beach tomorrow.

3 a is a polar bear.
  b was built a long time ago.
  c is in the library.   d licked my hand.
  e are coming to my party.

Week 25, Day 1
Pg 132

From early times people have set sail on the oceans to explore the unknown. Some explorers looked for new lands to settle. Others looked for fame, treasure, or adventure.

Long before science helped us understand the oceans, people thought the Earth was flat. Sailors believed that if they sailed far enough, they would fall off the edge of the world. Of course they never did, but storms, pirates, and hidden reefs meant that some ships did sink to the bottom of the sea. Today, adventurers go in search of sunken treasure!

1 c   2 b   3 a   4 d

Week 25, Day 2
Pg 133

> People have always caught fish and other sea creatures using (baskets) (hooks), and (nets)
> Today large fishing boats can catch, clean, and freeze fish while still at sea.
>
> Modern fishing boats take huge amounts of seafood from the sea. Popular ocean fish that people eat include tuna, herring, sardines, cod, and snapper. Every year about 75 million tons of fish are caught worldwide.
>
> Seaweed is also harvested. People eat it raw or cooked and sometimes use it to thicken foods such as ice cream and yogurt. Seaweed can also be used to make toothpaste and sausages!

1 three different methods for catching fish are listed: baskets, hooks, nets

2 the facts about the "huge" amounts of seafood harvested each year: Every year about 75 million tonnes of fish are caught worldwide

3 very useful because versatile

Week 25, Day 3
Pg 134

1 Check for correct spelling of each word.

2 a dangerous **b** tremendous **c** previous
d generous **e** nervous

3 Missing letters are underlined
a danger<u>ous</u> **b** fur<u>ious</u> **c** <u>t</u>remend<u>ous</u>
d ser<u>ious</u> **e** v<u>a</u>rious **f** del<u>icious</u>
g mysteri<u>ous</u> **h** obv<u>ious</u> **i** cur<u>ious</u>
j ca<u>u</u>tious **k** <u>j</u>ealous **l** gener<u>ous</u>
m advent<u>urous</u> **n** f<u>a</u>bulous **o** glamor<u>ous</u>
p prec<u>ious</u> **q** humor<u>ous</u> **r** ner<u>vous</u>

4 a precious **b** various **c** famous
d dangerous **e** curious **f** obvious

Week 25, Day 4
Pg 135

1 a nervous **b** generous **c** humorous
d obvious **e** delicious **f** cautious
g previous

2 Check for correct spelling of each word.

3 a anxious **b** precarious **c** luxurious
d treacherous **e** hideous

4 a disastrous **b** ridiculous **c** gorgeous
d spacious **e** hideous

Week 25, Day 5
Pg 136

1 Check a, c, f

2 a I got a kitten for my birthday. I was so happy.
b We knew it would rain soon. The clouds were getting darker and heavier.

3 a I dropped the stone in the pond, and it sank to the bottom.
b I put new batteries in the toy, but it still didn't work.

Week 26, Day 1
Pg 137

> Most scientists believe that we should be concerned about global warming. Firstly, they say measurements taken on Earth and in space show that the average temperature is getting higher. They attribute this rise in temperature to the gases released into the atmosphere when fossil fuels are burned. Secondly, the warmer temperatures are causing vast chunks of ice to melt around the north and south poles, resulting in rising sea levels. This could lead to coastal areas and low-lying land being swamped. Finally, they point to the shrinking of glaciers in many parts of the world.

1 d **2** b **3** c **4** a

Week 26, Day 2
Pg 138

> But there are some scientists who believe that global warming is a natural process that has been happening for the last 6,000 years. The average temperature today, they say, is approximately 11 degrees warmer than it was back then, but it has been rising gradually since that time, not suddenly in the last 100 years. These scientists blame global warming on the way our planets are aligned and the effect they have on our orbit, and that is something we have no control over.
>
> As for me, I have always preferred to err on the side of caution, so I will continue to switch off lights and do whatever I can to reduce my carbon footprint on the planet.

1 It is a natural process that has been occurring over the last 6,000 years. They believe it is because of the way the planets are aligned and how that affects Earth's orbit. These are factors outside of our control.

2 the actions like switching off lights will reduce his or her carbon footprint and in time this will help reduce the impact of global warming

Week 26, Day 3
Pg 139

1 Check for correct spelling of each word.

2 a immobile **b** incurable **c** illegal
d incomplete **e** invisible **f** impolite
g insecure

3 a imperfect **b** illegal **c** inaccurate
d incurable **e** impersonal **f** impossible
g invisible **h** immature

4

in	im	ir	il
inactive	impure	irregular	illegal
invisible	immobile		illogical
incomplete	impolite		
insecure	imperfect		
incorrect	impossible		
inaccurate	impatient		
incurable	immature		
infertile	immortal		
	impersonal		

Week 26, Day 4
Pg 140

1 a <u>im</u>correct incorrect **b** <u>in</u>llogical illogical
c <u>il</u>visible invisible **d** <u>im</u>llegal illegal
e <u>in</u>rregular irregular **f** <u>in</u>polite impolite
g <u>il</u>patient impatient

2 Check for correct spelling of each word.

3 a impartial **b** insincere **c** illegible
d imbalance **e** irreplaceable **f** irrelevant
g impractical **h** illiterate

4 a insincere **b** irresponsible **c** illegible
d improbable **e** impractical

Week 26, Day 5
Pg 141

1 a so/and **b** but/yet **c** yet/but **d** and/but

2 a (but) **b** (yet) **c** (so) **d** (or)

3 a <u>I was feeling sick</u>, so <u>I went to the doctor.</u>
b <u>She wanted a red bike</u>, but <u>they were sold out.</u>
c <u>You can have a smartphone</u>, or <u>you can have a laptop.</u>
d <u>I carried the groceries into the kitchen</u> and <u>he unpacked them.</u>

4 a compound **b** simple **c** simple
d compound

Week 27, Day 1
Pg 142

> Many reef fish have bright colors. This provides them with good camouflage. Colorful spots and stripes make them difficult to see among the coral. Some fish can even change their color to hide from predators. Others, such as trumpetfish, are predators that change color to trick their prey

1 b **2** d **3** a **4** a, c **5** d

Week 27, Day 2
Pg 143

> Coral reefs are fragile and they need to be protected. There are some natural threats to coral reefs, but people cause the most damage.
>
> Coral needs clear water to grow. When forests are cut down on land, erosion washes soil into the ocean. The plants inside the corals stop growing and the corals begin to die.
>
> Pollution caused by industry and shipping can also poison coral polyps. Ships leak fuel into the water and the boat anchors break off coral. Oil spills can cause huge damage as well.

1 that fragile things need to be treated carefully at all times

2 erosion is when soil wears away and is carried to another place by the wind or water

3 harmful or poisonous things to the natural environment like fuel and oil

ANSWERS • Weeks 27–28

Week 27, Day 3
Pg 144

1 Check for correct spelling of each word.

2 a collection **b** confession **c** limitation
d prevention **e** confusion **f** inspection
3 a education **b** temptation **c** alteration
d selection **e** inspection **f** election
g reaction **h** action **i** translation

4

act	action
collect	collection
confuse	confusion
educate	education
select	selection
direct	direction
create	creation

Week 27, Day 4
Pg 145

1 a location **b** temptation **c** discussion
d protection **e** election **f** direction
g translation
2 Check for correct spelling of each word.
3 a illustration **b** exaggeration
c information **d** determination
e abbreviation **f** possession
g expression **h** imagination
4 a exaggeration **b** information
c determination **d** imagination
e congratulation

Week 27, Day 5
Pg 146

1 a so **b** but **c** or **d** and
2 a The door was open, so we went inside.
b Tom hit the ball hard, but Marcus caught it.
c The children were cold, so they went inside.
d My bird is sick, so tomorrow I will take her to the vet.
e We can eat at home, or we can try the new restaurant.
f Amelia has tidied her room, but she is jumping on the bed.
g I have made my mother a card, and I have bought her a present.
3 Check: b, c, f

REVIEW 3
Spelling

1 a fracture **b** honor **c** dolphins
d mountain **e** imagine **f** chef
2 a **3** selection
4 a phrase **b** spaghetti **c** whisk **d** hyphen
5 a wept **b** ridden
6 a impolite **b** illegal **c** inaccurate **d** irregular
7 bicycle

Grammar

1 a "Let's go for a swim," said Andy.
b Marty said, "Please put the milk back in the fridge."
2 a their, there **b** Where, were **c** here, hear
3 a How quickly can you say "She sells seashells on the seashore?"
b On the front of the card it said "Happy birthday!"
4 a Maxine said that she had never been to California.
b Will asked me if I had a dog.
5 a might **b** will **c** must **d** can
6 a The yellow butterfly has landed on that flower.
b My parents are taking me to Mount Rushmore.
7 a Answers will vary. Suggested answer: I love basketball. I would play every day if I could.
b Answers will vary. Suggested answer: I left the keys on the table, but someone must have taken them.
8 a It started to rain, so I put up my umbrella.
b I looked everywhere for my book, but I couldn't find it.
c I put my socks in the drawer and I put my shirt in the cupboard.

Comprehension

1 b **2** d **3** c **4** c **5** c, d
6 Answers will vary. Suggested answer:
The text says that "He [Kelly] jumps back in fright as it begins to make a noise." This tells us Kelly is scared by the ticking sound. The text also says, "Suddenly, the yellow thing wraps itself around his leg. Now Kelly is really frightened!" The word frightened and the exclamation point emphasize that Kelly is scared of the pocket watch.
7 a
8 Answers will vary. Suggested answer:
The watch likely dropped into the furrow as Farmer Flynn worked in the fields.

Week 28, Day 1
Pg 152

> From now on Sarah's home would be a large, traveling space station. The shuttle was taking them to the big mother ship, Star Wanderer. It would carry all three hundred of them towards Alpha Centauri, and a lifetime of new discoveries.
>
> Suddenly Sarah was scared. It was such an unknown future that lay ahead—like it was for those sailors, hundreds of years ago, sailing over the edge of the Earth.

1 Answers will vary. Ask children to talk through responses.
2 Answers will vary. Ask children to talk through responses.

Week 28, Day 2
Pg 153

> "We've all left a lot behind us," started Sarah, and many faces grew serious. Dr. Singh was worried. Was Sarah going to remind them too much of earthly celebrations?
>
> "For me, the most important part of Christmas is the Christmas tree. Every year I'd dream about what it would look like. I couldn't wait until it was time to start decorating it." Sarah continued, "Kapil and I have something special that comes from Earth. Something from the past to take us into the future."
>
> Sarah signalled to Kapil, who tugged a cord.
>
> The curtain fell. In front of them was a young apple tree, holding its branches and green leaves high. Seven red apples hung from the branches.

1 Answers will vary. Ask children to talk through responses.

Week 28, Day 3
Pg 154

1 Check for correct spelling of each word.
2 a regroup **b** prewash **c** readjust
d prepack **e** reappoint **f** prehistory
g reissue **h** delouse **i** premature
3 a replay **b** prepay **c** delouse
d premature **e** redo **f** debone
g prehistory **h** defuse

4

re		de	pre
redo	reroute	decode	prepack
rearrange	reappoint	debrief	prepay
redirect		debone	prewash
replay		delouse	premature
regroup		defuse	prehistory
reboot			
readjust			
rephrase			

Week 28, Day 4
Pg 155

1 a deacode decode **b** debreef debrief
c defuze defuse **d** reearange rearrange
e deebone debone **f** redoe redo
g prepaye prepay **h** refrase rephrase
2 Check for correct spelling of each word.
3 a repopulate **b** reupholster **c** regain
d rebroadcast **e** demystify
4 a regain **b** reissue **c** reupholster
d reassemble

Week 28, Day 5
Pg 156

1 Check: a, b, f, g, i, j, l
2 a if the shoe fits **b** because it's delicious
c before the rain starts
3 a If **b** Although **c** because
d until **e** when **f** unless

213

Week 29, Day 1
Pg 157

> I must be the (worst) fisherkid on Earth!
> It isn't that I don't try. Every chance
> I get, I'm dangling a line in the water
> somewhere. My bookshelves are full
> of every fishing book and fishing map
> ever printed. I buy the best fishing line
> pocket money can buy. And I watch all
> the fishing reports on TV and listen to
> them on the radio as well.

1 c **2** a **3** c **4** d

Week 29, Day 2
Pg 158

> The fishing report suddenly becomes
> very serious. The reporter is warning
> people about the dangers of fishing from
> a popular local spot. Two fishermen have
> gone missing. The camera zooms in on the
> spot where the fishermen were last seen.
>
> I know the spot — it's called Devil's
> Rocks. It's a good spot to catch kingfish.
> Suddenly, a huge wave comes out of
> nowhere and crashes over the rocky ledge.

1 the reporter says, "a popular local spot"

2 the fishing spot is called Devil's Rocks and during the report a huge wave crashes over the rocky ledge

3 the text says, "the fishing report suddenly becomes serious", and "the camera zooms in"

4 the text says, "a huge wave comes out of nowhere and crashes over the rocky ledge"

Week 29, Day 3
Pg 159

1 Check for correct spelling of each word.

2 a boredom **b** statement **c** brotherhood
d adulthood **e** childhood **f** agreement
g leadership **h** hardship **i** retirement

3 a kingdom **b** boredom **c** freedom
d childhood **e** argument

4

agree	agreement
excite	excitement
brother	brotherhood
leader	leadership
child	childhood
enjoy	enjoyment
king	kingdom
wise	wisdom

Week 29, Day 4
Pg 160

1 a excitement/enjoyment **b** freedom
c movement **d** argument **e** enjoyment
f statement **g** kingdom

2 Check for correct spelling of each word.

3 a equipment **b** government
c improvement **d** announcement
e entertainment **f** championship
g livelihood **h** arrangement

4 a improvement **b** announcement
c championship **d** arrangement
e entertainment **f** equipment

Week 29, Day 5
Pg 161

1 a who **b** that **c** which **d** whose
e who **f** that

2 a boys (who) **b** cake (which)
c sandwiches (that) **d** boy (whose)

3 a I haven't seen the movie that you are talking about.
b That's the pilot who will fly the plane.
c My parents gave me a bike, which was the best present I'd ever had.
d I sympathized with the girl whose mother was in hospital.

4 a *Answers will vary. Suggested answer:*
The people who signed the petition are in the hall.
b *Answers will vary. Suggested answer:*
The man whose car this is is over there.

Week 30, Day 1
Pg 162

> Leaving the brilliant sunshine, it took
> a while for his eyes to adjust to the
> inky blackness. The hairs on the back
> of his neck (bristled). Unaware that he
> was holding his breath, Spook inched
> forward, his shoes scraping on the earth.
> His fists were clenched. His fingernails
> bit into his palms.
>
> The cave was narrow inside. Cobwebs
> veiled the walls like gauze.

1 c **2** b **3** d **4** a **5** b

Week 30, Day 2
Pg 163

> Feet barely contacting the ground, the
> boys (bolted)—chased by the scream.
> Spook was in the lead, then Nathan
> and, well behind, Aaron, his short legs
> hardly able to keep pace. Branches and
> thorns stabbed and snatched at them.
> Long grass tickled their legs like creepy
> crawlies.
>
> Eventually, out of breath, the trio
> stopped. They doubled over and
> gasped for air and their legs ached.

1 bolted

2 that the thorns were intentionally vicious

3 the grass touched them lightly, making them feel uncomfortable

4 short, raspy, noisy breaths

Week 30, Day 3
Pg 164

1 Check for correct spelling of each word.

2 a fishery **b** salary **c** voluntary
d slavery **e** directory **f** ivory
g glossary **h** cutlery **i** pottery

3 a celery **b** salary **c** pottery
d February **e** robbery **f** cutlery
g surgery

4 a robary robbery **b** boundory boundary
c secondery secondary **d** cellery celery
e hestory history **f** seenery scenery
g volentery voluntary

Week 30, Day 4
Pg 165

1 a February **b** cutlery **c** glossary
d ivory **e** artery **f** surgery
g pottery

2 Check for correct spelling of each word.

3 a embroidery **b** anniversary
c temporary **d** confectionary
e extraordinary **f** finery
g customary **h** observatory

4 a treachery **b** embroidery
c observatory **d** anniversary
e customary **f** temporary

Week 30, Day 5
Pg 166

1 a where **b** why **c** when **d** where
e why **f** when

2 a town (where) **b** reason (why) **c** night (when)
d place (where) **e** time (when)

3 a *Answers will vary. Suggested answer:*
We searched the room where the toys were kept.
b *Answers will vary. Suggested answer:*
I know the reason why people love to eat cake.
c *Answers will vary. Suggested answer:*
Twelve o'clock is the hour when I'm hungry for lunch.
d *Answers will vary. Suggested answer:*
The children went to the beach where they looked for shells.

Week 31, Day 1
Pg 167

> "How lucky am I," said Eagle, "that I have
> such (powers of flight to take me so high) and
> so far. There is no mountain too high for me!
> Here I am, looking down on all the world
> from a height no other living creature has
> ever reached!"
>
> "What a boaster you are," said Spider, from
> a nearby twig. "Look where I am sitting. It
> isn't so far below you, is it?" Spider jumped
> to another twig, just above Eagle's head. He
> began to busily spin a web, just above Eagle.
>
> "How did you reach this height?" asked Eagle.
> "You are weak and wingless. Did you somehow
> manage to crawl all the way up here?"

1 b **2** c **3** a **4** d

Week 31, Day 2
Pg 168

> "How did you reach this height?" asked Eagle. "You are weak and wingless. Did you somehow manage to crawl all the way up here?"
>
> "No!" laughed Spider. "I simply attached myself to you, and you lifted me from the valleys below on your tail feathers. And I can get along very well without your help too, now that I am way up here. So, Eagle, don't put on any airs with me, because I want to tell you that ..."
>
> Suddenly, a gust of wind swept across the top of the mountain. It slid right by Eagle but it brushed Spider, web and all, back down into the depths of the valley.

1 Eagle flew up to the top of the mountain. Spider attached himself to Eagle, so Spider could reach the top of the mountain.

2 Eagle is heavier than Spider

3 Spider is light and couldn't withstand the higher wind speed at the top of the mountain

Week 31, Day 3
Pg 169

1 Check for correct spelling of each word.

2 **a** predictable **b** advisable **c** comfortable **d** respectable **e** enjoyable **f** adjustable **g** affordable

3 Missing letters are underlined
a suit<u>able</u> **b** afford<u>able</u> **c** sens<u>ible</u>
d adjust<u>able</u> **e** bear<u>able</u> **f** terr<u>ible</u>
g valu<u>able</u> **h** adjust<u>able</u> **i** reli<u>able</u>
j enjoy<u>able</u> **k** accept<u>able</u> **l** favor<u>able</u>
m fashion<u>able</u> **n** reason<u>able</u>

4 **a** suitable **b** adjustable **c** fashionable **d** reliable **e** sensible **f** predictable

Week 31, Day 4
Pg 170

1 **a** sensible **b** comfortable
c sensible/suitable/comfortable
d flexible **e** enjoyable
f terrible **g** suitable

2 Check for correct spelling of each word.

3 **a** imaginable **b** believable **c** admirable **d** noticeable **e** manageable **f** divisible **g** avoidable **h** reversible

4 **a** reversible **b** believable **c** accessible **d** imaginable **e** noticeable

Week 31, Day 5
Pg 171

1 **a** relative adverb **b** relative pronoun
c relative adverb **d** relative pronoun
e relative pronoun **f** relative adverb

2 **a** where the famous actor lives
b why the lights are flickering
c who broke the window
d that I bought online
e when everything went wrong
f which have leather covers

3 **a** *Answers will vary. Suggested answer:* I met him at the shop where we were both buying comics.

b *Answers will vary. Suggested answer:* The President presented the prize to the athlete who won three Olympic gold medals.

c *Answers will vary. Suggested answer:* They towed away the car that was parked illegally.

Week 32, Day 1
Pg 172

> Hoover Dam controls the flow of the Colorado River. It is on the border between the states of Arizona and Nevada.
>
> Work on the dam began in 1931. Men poured concrete 24 hours a day, seven days a week. The dam was completed in 1935, more than two years ahead of schedule.
>
> Hoover Dam allowed more people to live in America's south-west. The reliable water supply is used for farming. Electricity from the dam's power station is used by people in three states.

1 d   2 c   3 b   4 c   5 a

Week 32, Day 2
Pg 173

> The Golden Gate Bridge is a suspension bridge across the opening of San Francisco Bay.
>
> Many people said a bridge could not be built there. There are strong currents in the bay, and the water is up to 330 feet deep. It is also a very windy and foggy site.
>
> The Golden Gate was the longest suspension bridge in the world when it was completed in 1937. The bridge's two main cables connect to each end of the bridge and hold up the road. Each one is made of more than 27,000 thinner cables.

1 San Francisco Bay

2 suspension bridge

3 330 feet

4 1937

5 the two main cables; each one is made of more than 27,000 smaller cables

Week 32, Day 3
Pg 174

1 Check for correct spelling of each word.

2 **a** scale **b** audience

3 **a** territory **b** manually **c** scribe **d** terrain **e** decimal **f** manicure **g** scribble **h** prescription

4 **a** audience **b** scale **c** terrain **d** decade **e** scribble **f** December **g** manicure

Week 32, Day 4
Pg 175

1 **a** <u>descrybe</u> describe
b <u>Descemba</u> December
c <u>manuel</u> manual **d** <u>awdition</u> audition
e <u>awdiance</u> audience **f** <u>scaile</u> scale
g <u>scribel</u> scribble **h** <u>mainager</u> manager

2 Check for correct spelling of each word.

3 **a** terrestrial **b** decibel **c** manufacture **d** escalate **e** terrarium **f** anniversary **g** territorial **h** subterranean

4 **a** subterranean **b** escalate **c** manipulate **d** manufacture **e** decibel

Week 32, Day 5
Pg 176

1 **a** ? **b** ! **c** ! **d** ? **e** ? **f** ! **g** ! **h** ? **i** ? **j** !

2 **a** *Answers will vary. Suggested answer:* How much flour do we need for the muffins?

b *Answers will vary. Suggested answer:* What time is the party?

3 **a** *Answers will vary. Suggested answer:* How wonderful was that!

b *Answers will vary. Suggested answer:* What a brilliant idea that is!

Week 33, Day 1
Pg 177

> Plants are an essential part of the ocean's food chains. Some sea creatures eat plants. Others are carnivores that eat other sea creatures.
>
> Food chains in the ocean begin with plankton. Plankton is a mixture of tiny animals and algae. Like all plants, the algae use the sun's energy to make food. Very small crustaceans feed on the tiny algae and together they are known as plankton.

> The word plankton is Greek for wanderer or drifter. It refers to a category of drifting organisms found in the middle and upper levels of the ocean.
>
> Plankton consists of algae, which live near the surface where they can draw on the sun's energy to make food, and tiny crustaceans that feed on the algae.
>
> Small creatures such as krill and shrimps feed on the plankton and larger fish eat the shrimps.

1 b, d, e

Week 33, Day 2
Pg 178

> The ocean floor has many of the same features you find on land. Mountain ranges, volcanoes, deep trenches, and wide, flat plains are all found on the ocean floor.
>
> When measured from the ocean floor, Hawaii's Mauna Kea rises more than 30,000 feet, making it the tallest mountain on Earth!
>
> Chains of underwater volcanoes, known as seamounts, exist on all ocean floors. Some islands are seamounts that have risen out of the ocean. The Hawaiian Islands are at the end of a chain of underwater volcanoes.

> The ocean floor is a mysterious world waiting to be explored. We know more about the surface of the moon and our closest planets! What we do know, however, is that the ocean floor has similar features to those found on land, such as mountains, volcanoes, and deep trenches.
>
> The tallest mountain in the world actually starts on the ocean floor. It's Mount Kea in Hawaii, which is about 14,000 feet above sea level. But below sea level it measures almost 16,000 feet, making it slightly higher than Mount Everest.

1 you can find mountains, volcanoes, and deep trenches

2 it is in Hawaii, and it is 30,000 feet above sea level

3 the islands are at the end of a chain of underwater volcanoes, known as seamounts

Week 33, Day 3
Pg 179

1 Check for correct spelling of each word.

2 **a** material **b** writing

3 **a** already **b** whose **c** guilty **d** question **e** writing **f** material **g** doesn't **h** position

4 **a** who **b** across **c** question **d** material **e** answer **f** guilty **g** Once **h** breathe

Week 33, Day 4
Pg 180

1 a <u>therefour</u> therefore **b** <u>Wonce</u> Once
c <u>havn't</u> haven't **d** <u>busie</u> busy
e <u>brethe</u> breathe **f** <u>intrest</u> interest
g <u>akross</u> across **h** <u>anser</u> answer
2 Check for correct spelling of each word.
3 a pollution **b** address **c** especially
d perhaps **e** suppose **f** purpose
g especially **h** neighbor
4 a favorite **b** pollution **c** address
d probably **e** neighbor

Week 33, Day 5
Pg 181

1 Replace periods in b, c, e
2 Remove exclamation points after sight, obeyed, surroundings
3 *Answers will vary. Suggested answer:*
I can't wait to go to the fair!

Week 34, Day 1
Pg 182

> Some people think that plunging down the side of a mountain on a pair of skis is the most exciting feeling in the world. People who do this are called speed skiers. They can reach speeds of 150 miles an hour.
> It takes cool nerves and top-notch protection to be a speed skier. Rocks, boulders, and trees can be deadly, so helmets are essential. Avalanches can also be a danger, so you need to carry a special light. Then you can be found and dug out of the snow if you are buried by an avalanche.
> Brothers Simone and Ivan Origone of Italy are world champion speed skiers. In 2016, Ivan set off down Chabrieres piste in the French resort of Vars. By the time he reached the bottom, Ivan had set a new world record of 156.424 miles per hour.

1 a F **b** O **c** F **d** F **e** O **f** F **g** F

Week 34, Day 2
Pg 183

> Caving takes us deep within the earth. It involves a lot of crawling, squeezing, sliding, and stooping, often in mud and water. It is not for people who are claustrophobic or who want to keep their clothes clean.
> But caving gives you the most amazing sights: gigantic chambers and deep black holes, underground lakes and rivers, and beautiful stalagmites and stalactites. Perhaps best of all, it makes you feel that you are in a place where no one else has been before.

1 Caving takes you deep into the Earth. Caving requires: crawling, squeezing, sliding and stooping, often in mud and water. Sights you can see: gigantic chambers, deep black holes, underground lakes and rivers, and beautiful stalagmites and stalactites.
2 The sites you see will be amazing. Stalagmites and stalactites are beautiful. Caving makes you feel that you are in a place where no one else has been before.

Week 34, Day 3
Pg 184

1 Check for correct spelling of each word.
2

heavy	heavily
simple	simply
gentle	gently
happy	happily
visible	visibly
sensible	sensibly
possible	possibly
noble	nobly
lucky	luckily
comfortable	comfortably
easy	easily

3 a basi<u>c</u>ally **b** remar<u>k</u>ably **c** hum<u>b</u>ly
d luck<u>ily</u> **e** sensi<u>b</u>ly **f** hap<u>p</u>ily
g reasonably **h** gently
4 *Answers will vary. Suggested answers:*
a simply **b** angrily **c** happily
d heavily **e** possibly **f** humbly

Week 34, Day 4
Pg 185

1 a <u>happely</u> happily
b <u>basecally</u> basically
c <u>Remarkebly</u> Remarkably
d <u>steedily</u> steadily
e <u>hestorically</u> historically
f <u>jently</u> gently
g <u>publikely</u> publicly
2 Check for correct spelling of each word.
3 a automatically **b** necessarily
c frantically **d** responsibly
e specifically **f** dramatically
g ordinarily **h** primarily
i enthusiastically
4 a specifically **b** automatically
c systematically **d** enthusiastically
e frantically

Week 34, Day 5
Pg 186

1 a it **b** after **c** unless **d** who
e while **f** which **g** but **h** because
2 a I've had lunch, but I'm still hungry.
b I will visit them if they are at home.
c I made an appointment before I went to see him.
d I will feed the dog while you unpack the dishwasher.

Week 35, Day 1
Pg 187

> Nuclear energy is released from the nucleus of a uranium atom, a very dense metal found in the ground. Nuclear energy produces more than 11% of the world's electricity. Supporters of nuclear energy argue that nuclear power stations are safe and much cleaner than fossil fuel power stations. However many countries are starting to rethink their nuclear energy programs due to disasters like Fukushima in 2011.
> More than one-third of human-made greenhouse gases come from fossil-fuel power stations. As people continue to use coal and oil to produce electricity and fuel for transport, the amount of greenhouse gas emissions will increase. Nuclear power stations do not emit these gases, although they do produce radioactive waste.

1 b **2** a, c

Week 35, Day 2
Pg 188

> **Important Dates in the History of Flight**
> **1903:** Orville and Wilbur Wright completed the first flight in an aircraft.
> **1919:** John Alcock and Arthur Brown completed the first nonstop flight across the Atlantic Ocean.
> **1927:** Charles Lindbergh completed the first solo, nonstop flight across the Atlantic Ocean.
> **1928:** Amelia Earhart became the first woman to fly across the Atlantic Ocean.
> **1961:** Yuri Gagarin became the first person to travel in space.
> **1969:** Neil Armstrong and Buzz Aldrin became the first people to walk on the moon.

1 they were both firsts for aircraft
2 both went across the Atlantic Ocean
3 Yuri Gagarin was the first person to travel in space, but Armstrong and Aldrin became the first people to walk on the moon

Week 35, Day 3
Pg 189

1 Check for correct spelling of each word.
2

cc	xc
accent	excellent
accept	excel
accuse	excite
accident	exclaim
success	excuse
accustom	exceed
acclaim	excess
account	exclude
accost	excavate
accelerate	excursion

3 a acclaim **b** accost **c** accustom
d success **e** excellent
4 a accuse **b** excavate **c** accident
d accelerate **e** excursion **f** exclude

Week 35, Day 4
Pg 190
1 a success **b** accept **c** accelerate
d exclude

2 Missing letters are <u>underlined</u> **a** <u>excellent</u>
b <u>excursion</u> **c** <u>account</u> **d** <u>accelerate</u>
e <u>accost</u> **f** <u>accustom</u> **g** <u>exclude</u>
h <u>accept</u> **i** <u>accent</u> **j** <u>excel</u>

3 Check for correct spelling of each word.

4 a accompany **b** accumulate **c** eccentric
d excruciating **e** accomplish **f** accessory
g accidentally **h** excerpt

5 a excruciating **b** accidentally **c** accessory
d excerpt **e** accompany **f** accomplish
g accumulate **h** excavation

Week 35, Day 5
Pg 191
1 a film **b** child **c** will not
d yes **e** goodbye **f** good morning

2 a have to **b** tasty **c** impolite
d wonderful **e** contact

3 Circle: I would, apologize, allowing my dog
to, destroy, a long time, very proud of, very
angry, Spotty and me, repay, please, Yours
sincerely

Week 36, Day 1
Pg 192

> What makes a small bug big? It's all to do
> with some very big numbers. Scientists have
> worked out that there could be 10 quintillion
> insects alive at any one time. That's
> 10,000,000,000,000,000,000 bugs or
> (1.6 billion) of them for every one of us. And
> about 8,000 new kinds are discovered each year.
>
> Some insects, such as locusts, move in huge
> hungry groups called swarms. Swarms can
> contain [thousands of millions] of locusts. To stay
> alive, every locust needs to eat its own body
> weight in food each day. A swarm of locusts
> strips trees bare and gobbles up crops. There is
> nothing left after a locust swarm has passed.

1 c **2** a **3** d **4** c

Week 36, Day 2
Pg 193

> The slash of a claw, the flick of a
> tongue, or a strike from out of nowhere
> can mean [life] or sudden [death.]
>
> There's a need for speed in the animal
> world. All creatures are part of a food
> chain. The trick here is catching what
> you like to eat but not getting caught
> by what likes to eat you.
>
> But fast isn't always about making a
> quick getaway. To get its food, the
> hummingbird (flaps very fast) to stay still!

1 The slash of a claw, the flick of a tongue, or
a strike from out of nowhere can mean life
or sudden death.

2 All creatures are part of a food chain.

3 *Answers will vary. Ask children to talk
through responses.*

Week 36, Day 3
Pg 194
1 Check for correct spelling of each word.

2 a television **b** octopus **c** telescope
d zoo

3 Missing letters are <u>underlined</u>
a homo<u>phone</u> **b** ge<u>ology</u> **c** <u>m</u>icroscope
d mono<u>logue</u> **e** <u>tele</u>scope **f** <u>octopus</u>
g <u>phonetic</u> **h** <u>microchip</u>

4 a microphone **b** octave **c** periscope
d dialogue **e** epilogue **f** logo
g telescope **h** microchip

Week 36, Day 4
Pg 195
1 a <u>tellescope</u> telescope **b** <u>oktopus</u> octopus
c <u>tellevision</u> television **d** <u>monologe</u> monologue
e <u>octaive</u> octave **f** <u>mikrochip</u> microchip
g <u>catalloge</u> catalog **h** <u>periskope</u> periscope

2 Check for correct spelling of each word.

3 a democrat **b** chronological **c** democracy
d epidemic **e** symphony **f** octahedron
g xylophone

4 a octahedron **b** saxophone **c** xylophone
d zoologist **e** chronological

Week 36, Day 5
Pg 196
1 a ? **b** ! **c** . **d** . **e** ? **f** !

2 a knife's **b** should've **c** .
d dog's **e** lesson,

3 Have you seen Mark's new puppy? It's so
cute! I'm going to ask my parents if I can
have one too.

REVIEW 4
Spelling
1 a breathe **b** forty **c** celery **d** history

2 d **3** question

4 a enjoy<u>ment</u> **b** adult<u>hood</u> **c** excite<u>ment</u>
d leader<u>ship</u>

5 a happily **b** sensible **c** angrily
d comfortable

6 a

7 a <u>ex</u>cellent **b** <u>suc</u>cess **c** <u>ex</u>cess
d a<u>ccuse</u>

Grammar
1 a if you buy a ticket.
b because she was cold.
c until someone wins.
d unless someone helps me.

2 a <u>which</u> **b** <u>who</u> **c** <u>that</u> **d** <u>whose</u>

3 a <u>the building</u> where **b** <u>a time</u> when

4 a I called out to the girl <u>who had dropped
her book.</u>
b Watch out for frogs <u>that have brightly
colored skins.</u>
c She'll be able to tell me <u>whose watch
this is.</u>
d We picked up the eggs <u>which had fallen
from the nest.</u>

5 a compound **b** complex **c** complex
d compound

6 a ! **b** ? **c** ? **d** !

7 Change periods to exclamation marks after
go (line 3) and MONSTROUS (line 7)

8 a (cops) police officers
b (kids) children
c (real smart) very clever
d (Me and Mark) Mark and I

9 a She picked up the child's toy.
b "How did you get here?" asked the man.

Comprehension
1 d **2** b

3 *Answers will vary. Suggested answer:*
The text tells us that "pollution can cause
disease or death."

4 a **5** a **6** c **7** c

8 *Answers will vary. Suggested answer:*
People could protect their ears by wearing
earplugs or earmuffs when in noisy areas.

Reading Eggs *Reading for Fourth Grade*
ISBN: 978-1-74215-350-6
Copyright Blake eLearning USA 2018

Published by:
Blake eLearning USA
37 West 26th Street,
Suite 201
New York, NY 10010

www.readingeggspress.com

Publisher: Katy Pike
Series writer: Laura Anderson
Series editor: Amy Russo
Editor: Megan Smith, Mark Stafford

Designed and typeset by The Modern Art Production Group
Printed by 1010 Printing International LTD